Challenge your pupils
using problem-solving questions from the
Primary Mathematics Challenge

The Mathematical Association

First published in 2007 by
The Mathematical Association

ISBN 0 906588 63 4

Printed in Great Britain by
Cromwell Press Ltd, Trowbridge, Wiltshire

Hodder Murray

www.hoddereducation.co.uk

How to use this book

These problems can be used in several different ways. Here are a few ideas:

1   selected by the teacher for homework, either choosing particular topics or at random

2   extension work in class, selecting problems relating to classwork

3   selecting a problem as a starter for investigative work

4   practice for the papers set in PMC which take place every November (primary schools only).

The problems

Over 200 multiple choice problems from a variety of mathematical topics are provided for use by teachers in primary (and secondary) schools. The aim is to provide interesting mathematical experiences using elementary mathematics topics. Many of the problems can lead to further investigative work.

There are four categories of problems: Easy, Harder, Puzzling and Very Challenging. Most pupils should be able to get the easy problems correct, while the challenging problems will test the brightest young mathematicians in the country!

Answers and Notes

Answers and brief notes are provided for all problems. There are also some ideas for follow up work and extended investigation.

Mathematical Health Warning!

The difficult and challenging problems in this book are difficult! Problems for each pupil should first be selected from the Easy section, and then to progress to the more difficult problems, rather than start with the harder problems. If pupils cannot get a grip on the harder multiple choice problems, they will just guess!

Contents

Easy problems

E1 How many tadpoles are there in this picture ?

    A 1   B 3   C 6   D 12   E cannot tell

E2 Calculate $1 - 1 + 1 - 1 + 1$

    A −1   B 0   C 1   D 2   E 5

E3 Calculate $1 + 2 + 3 + 4$

    A 8   B 9   C 10   D 12   E 24

E4 $1 + 11 + 111 + 1111 =$

    A 10   B 1111   C 4321   D 1234   E 11111

E5 What is the value of $2 \times 2 \times 2$?

    A 2   B 6   C 8   D 222   E none of these

E6 Which has the answer 49?

    A 2×25 B 4×12 C 5×10 D 6×8 E 7×7

E7 What are the missing numbers in this table?

×	2	3	5
6	12	18	
2	4		10
4	8	12	20

    A 4 and 35   B 6 and 30   C 8 and 30

        D 6 and 35   E 8 and 35

E8 How many of these fractions are more than $\frac{1}{2}$?

$$\frac{1}{4} \qquad \frac{3}{8} \qquad \frac{1}{2} \qquad \frac{3}{4} \qquad \frac{7}{8}$$

    A 1   B 2   C 3   D 4   E 5

E9 What is $\frac{1}{2}$ of $\frac{1}{2}$?

    A 0   B $\frac{1}{4}$ C $\frac{1}{2}$ D $\frac{2}{4}$ E 1

E10 Which fraction has the largest value?

    A $\frac{1}{2}$ B $\frac{2}{3}$ C $\frac{3}{4}$ D $\frac{4}{5}$ E $\frac{5}{6}$

Easy problems

E11 What fraction is shaded?

A $\dfrac{3}{8}$ B $\dfrac{3}{5}$ C $\dfrac{5}{8}$ D $\dfrac{2}{3}$ E $\dfrac{3}{4}$

E12 The number six hundred and seven thousand, two hundred and three can be written as:

A 600 723 B 672 003 C 670 230 D 670 203 E 607 203

E13 What number comes next in this sequence: 2, 2, 4, 6, 10, 16, 26, □ ?

A 30 B 36 C 42 D 46 E 52

E14 Which gives the largest answer?

A 6×9 B 5×10 C $27 + 26$ D $18 + 35$ E Half of 110.

E15 How many multiples of 5 are less than 44?

A 6 B 7 C 8 D 9 E 10

E16 I am an adult cat. Which of these could be my age ?

A 5 seconds B 5 minutes C 5 weeks
D 5 years E 5 centuries

E17 What is the correct name of this shape?
A parallollygram B paellagram
C parallelogram D pparrallelloggrramm
E passthesaltgranny

E18 Which of these shapes is the parallelogram?

A B C D E

2

Easy problems

E19 Which shape is a hexagon?

A ☐ B ○ C ☐ D ⬭ E ⬡

E20 I start in this small maze at X. Which set of compass directions will get me out?

A S,E,S   B N,E,S   C W,N,E
D N,W,S   E W,S,E

E21 Which shape is different *in area* from the others?

A   B   C   D   E

E22 If you looked in the direction of the arrow, what would you see?

A ☐ B ▭ C ○ D ◺ E △

E23 A goat called Billy eats grass. He is tied by a chain to a ring attached to a long wall. What is the best description of the shape of the grass which Billy can eat?

A circle   B semicircle   C triangle
D square   E rectangle

E24 *C* is the centre of the rectangle. What fraction is shaded?

A $\frac{1}{4}$ B $\frac{1}{3}$ C $\frac{3}{8}$ D $\frac{1}{2}$ E $\frac{3}{4}$

E25 How many bricks are used to build this small tunnel?

A 15   B 20   C 24   D 25   E 26

Easy problems

E26 Which is a possible mirror reflection of the word ALICE?

∀ΓICE	ƎƆI⅃∀	ECILA	ƎƆI⅃A	ƎƆI⅃A
A	B	C	D	E

E27 About how high is a normal house door ?

A 1 m   B 2 m   C 3 m   D 5 m   E 10 m

E28 Patty bakes 1000 pasties to sell. She sells 513 pasties. How many has she got left?

A 487   B 513   C 596   D 597   E 1513

E29 If a snail travels 10 metres in 2 hours, how many metres will it travel in 5 hours if it keeps up the same speed ?

A 5   B 15   C 25   D 30   E 50

E30 If monkeys eat 10 bananas each day, how many would five monkeys eat in one day?

A 2   B 4   C 10   D 50   E 100

E31 Marcia will be 11 years old on 1st December 2003. In what year was she born?

A 1992   B 1993   C 1994   D 1995   E 1996

E32 Once upon a time there used to be 12 pence in a shilling. How many pence were there in 5 shillings?

A 5   B 12   C 20   D 24   E 60

E33 I start watching television at 4.50 pm and finish watching it at 5.40 pm. How long do I spend watching?

A 50 min   B 1 hr   C 1 hr 10 min   D 90 min   E 110 min

E34 Max has a 1p coin, a 2p coin and a 5p coin. Which sum of money can he *not* make ?

A 4p   B 5p   C 6p   D 7p   E 8p

Harder problems

H1 What is twelve thousand plus twelve hundred plus twelve?

    A 12 121   B 13 212   C 121 212   D 132 012   E 1 212 012

H2 What is $12\,345\,679 \times 9$?

    A 111 111 111   B 222 222 222   C 333 333 333
    D 444 444 444   E 555 555 555

H3 Which of these equals 1 ?

    A $1^2 + 1^2$ B $1^2 - 1^2$ C $2^2 - 1^2$ D $3^2 - 2^2$ E $2^2 \div 2^2$

H4 Which is the biggest?

    A 0^5 B 1^4 C 2^3 D 3^2 E 4^1

H5 What is $4000 \div \frac{1}{2}$?

    A 80   B 200   C 800   D 2000   E 8000

H6 How many of these calculations equal 1 ?

    ½ + ½   ½ − ½   ½ × ½   ½ ÷ ½
    A 0   B 1   C 2   D 3   E 4

H7 I was given a 1500-piece jigsaw of Albert Einstein.
Half the pieces are missing and half of the rest are
damaged. How many good pieces are there?

    A 0   B 350   C 375   D 500   E 750

H8 Afsal eats half his cake. He then give a $\frac{1}{4}$ of what is left to a friend.
What fraction of the original cake is left ?

    A $\frac{3}{4}$ B $\frac{3}{8}$ C $\frac{5}{8}$ D $\frac{1}{2}$ E $\frac{7}{8}$

H9 Which number is NOT a factor of 101 010 ?

    A 2   B 3   C 5   D 7   E 11

Harder problems

H10 One of these numbers is not factor of 2004. Which one?

    A 2   B 3   C 4   D 5   E 6

H11 Which number is not a factor of 2005?

    A 1   B 5   C 25   D 401   E 2005

H12 Pills are sold in rectangular arrays like this pack of 8 pills. Which number could only make a long thin pack of pills?

    A 12   B 13   C 14   D 15   E 16

H13 I am thinking of a number less than 40. It is an even number, a multiple of 3 and a multiple of 5. What is the number ?

    A 9   B 15   C 20   D 30   E 35

H14 How many square numbers are there between 0 and 20?

    A 1   B 2   C 3   D 4   E 5

H15 What do all these numbers have in common ?

    64   121   289   625

    A They are all odd numbers   B They are all less than 625
    C They are all prime numbers   D They are all divisible by 3
    E They are all square numbers

H16 12 children share some biscuits. They each take 3 biscuits and eat them. Which calculation will allow me to work out how many biscuits there were altogether ?

    A 12 + 3   B 12 × 3   C 12 − 3   D 12 ÷ 3   E 1 + 2 + 3

H17 The answer to 5 × 8 × 9 is the same as the answer to one of the questions below. Which one?

    A 8 × 14   B 40 × 5   C 72 × 5   D 13 × 9   E 17 × 5

Harder problems

H18 What time does this anti-clockwise clock show?

    A 4.45   B 5.15   C 7.15   D 7.45   E 9.25

H19 Look at these clocks. Which one would show the time 10.35 if rotated 180° about the centre?

A   B   C   D   E

H20 I fold a rectangle along its diagonal. What outline shape do I get?

    A triangle   B kite   C square
    D pentagon   E hexagon

H21 What fraction of this regular hexagon is shaded ?

    A $\dfrac{1}{6}$ B $\dfrac{1}{4}$ C $\dfrac{1}{3}$ D $\dfrac{1}{2}$ E $\dfrac{2}{3}$

H22 I have a square piece of paper and fold it twice. Which shape can't I get?

    A square   B rectangle   C triangle
    D kite   E circle

H23 One side of an isosceles triangle is 5 cm long. Another side is 13 cm long. How long is the third side?

    A 5 cm   B 7 cm   C 12 cm D 13 cm E more information
                                         is required

H24 If the area of a square is 100 cm², what is the length of one of its sides ?

    A 1 cm   B 10 cm   C 20 cm   D 50 cm   E 100 cm

Harder problems

H25 Boris the spider weaves a circular web of circumference 40 cm. The web is made of sections where the angle at the centre is exactly 45 degrees.

If he travels around the edge of one of the sections of his web, how far will he have travelled?

A 5 cm   B 8 cm   C 10 cm   D 15 cm   E 24 cm

H26 The diagram shows centimetre cubes arranged into a bigger cube with holes all the way through. How many centimetre cubes are there in the model?

A 7   B 20   C 22   D 24   E 27

H27 Which of these solid shapes will not tessellate in three dimensions?

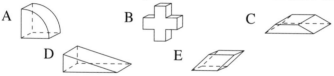

H28 How many lines of symmetry does a chess board have?

A 1   B 2   C 3   D 4   E 5

H29 How many of these 11 letters have at least one line of symmetry ?

MEASUREMENT

A 0   B 6   C 7   D 8   E 9

H30 Suppose $\frac{2}{5}$ of people are left-handed. How many left-handed people would you expect to find in a group of 55 people on a coach?

A 2   B 11   C 22   D 25   E 30

Harder problems

H31 This pie chart shows how much pocket money three children are given each week. Colin has £5 a week. How much do Ruth and Peter get altogether?

A £5   B £7.50   C £10   D £15   E £20

H32 WillyWontey can't decide which offer to take when buying doughnuts. They are all priced at 50p each but shops offer different bargains. Which shop gives the best value?

A 3 for the price of 2   B 5 for the price of 4
C 2 for the price of 3   D 5 for the price of 3
E 1 for the price of 6

H33 Yasmin wants to buy some small biscuit teddies. Which of these gives the cheapest price in pence per teddy?

A 10p each   B 2 for 18p   C 3 for 26p
D 4 for 35p   E 5 for 44p

H34 Lee cycled the 2 miles to his Gran's house at a speed of 10 mph. He got there at 11 am. At what time did he start?

A 10.00   B 10.32   C 10.40   D 10.48   E 10.50

H35 If I can travel 35 miles on 1 gallon of fuel and my tank holds 8 gallons, how many miles can I travel on a tank of fuel ?

A 70   B 140   C 280   D 560   E 1120

H36 Three Googleblips have twenty-seven tentacles altogether. If they all have the same number of tentacles as each other, how many tentacles do five Googleblips have?

A 9   B 27   C 40   D 45   E impossible to say

Harder problems

H37 Some sloths have three toes on each foot.
They have four feet each. How many
toes are there on two of these sloths?

A 6   B 7   C 12   D 24   E 40

H38 It takes Irem half an hour to do her maths homework, and half of that
to learn her spellings. If she starts homework at 4.10pm and has a
five minute break in the middle of her homework, when does she
finish?

A 4.40pm   B 4.55pm   C 5pm   D 5.25pm   E 5.30pm

H39 Not-so-simple Simon sold seven sweets for
seventy seven pence each. How much
money did he receive?

A 11p   B 77p   C £5.39   D £7.77   E £53.90

H40 A shepherd had 17 sheep. All but 9 died. How
many did he have left?

A 0   B 8   C 9   D 17   E 26

H41 I go to sleep at 8pm, wake up at 5.50am the next day, go back to
sleep at 6.05am, and wake up for good at 7.01am. How long did I
sleep for altogether?

A 8hr 44min   B 8hr 46min   C 9hr 04min
D 10hr 46min   E none of these time

H42 My brainy brother and sister added their ages together and got 15.
When they multiplied their ages together, they got 54. How old are
they?

A 3 and 5   B 5 and 10   C 6 and 9   D 7 and 8   E both 7½

Harder problems

H43 Dina Myte likes bottles of a fizzy drink called Phiizz. She can drink one bottle in 2 minutes. If she could drink 100 bottles at the same rate without any breaks and with nothing unusual happening, how long would it take?

A less than one hour   B 1hr 40min   C 1hr 42min

D 2hr   E 3hr 20min

H44 If the day before yesterday was Wednesday, what will be the day after tomorrow?

A Tuesday   B April   C Saturday

D Sunday   E Impossible to say

H45 Freda fries four fish in five minutes, and Fred fries five fish in four minutes. How many fish are fried if they both fry for twenty minutes?

A 9   B 20   C 40   D 41   E 50

H46 Tim takes two minutes to tie up three twigs; Tom takes three minutes to tie up two twigs. How many more twigs (than Tom) does Tim tie in thirty minutes?

A 5   B 20   C 25   D 45   E 65

H47 Nellie the elephant always eats 50 peanuts as a treat each feeding time at 2 pm, 4 pm and 6pm on Mondays, Wednesdays, Fridays and Saturdays. How many peanuts does the keeper need to buy for a week's supply?

A 150   B 300   C 450   D 600   E 750

H48 Imagine a world which can have a negative number of people. A bus in this world had 5 passengers. Then nine got off. Then six more got on. How many passengers are on the bus now?

A −20   B −2   C 0   D 2   E 20

Harder problems

H49 What page number will be printed on the back page of a newspaper made from 6 sheets of paper folded in half ?

A 6   B 12   C 18   D 20   E 24

H50 Aaron, Ben and Carl went shopping. Ben had 10p more than Aaron and Aaron had 10p more than Carl. They put all their money together to buy a ball for £1.20. How much did Aaron have at the beginning?

A 20p   B 30p   C 40p   D 50p   E 60p

H51 A shop sells National Lottery tickets. You see the sentence 'It could be you'. What is the chance that someone, with one ticket, will win a large prize with a National Lottery ticket?

A impossible   B very unlikely   C unlikely
D evens   E likely

H52 Vicky Vosene is planning to have a bath. Suppose V = get out of the bath, W = wash myself, X = get in the bath, Y = put the water in, and Z = dry myself. Which is the correct order for a successful bath?

A VWXYZ   B ZYXWV   C WZXVY
D YXWZV   E YXWVZ

H53 I am thinking of two numbers. When I add them I get 14. When I take one from the other, I get 6. What is the larger number?

A 6   B 8   C 10   D 14   E 20

H54 3 and 4 are to 12 as 4 and 5 are to what ?

A 12   B 20   C 21   D 45   E 54

Puzzling problems

P1 Jamal tried to work out 12.7 + 3.85 on a calculator but he made a mistake and got the answer 397.7. Which of these is most likely to have been his mistake?

A He pressed × instead of +   B He pressed 21.7 instead of 12.7
C He pressed − instead of +   D He pressed 35.8 instead of 38.5
E He missed out one of the decimal points.

P2 Mick Sterbs the gardener plants 30 rows of beans, 20 rows of carrots and 15 rows of cabbages. Each row has 20 plants. How many plants has he planted altogether?

A 600   B 700   C 900   D 1000   E 1300

P3 A group of four girls is having problems. J dislikes K and L. L dislikes J and M. K dislikes L and M, and M dislikes L. Which two girls get on well together?

A J and M   B L and M   C J and K
D K and L   E L and J

P4 European countries use the Indian/Arabic way of writing numbers, but our symbols look different now. In Arabic the number 427 is written ۴۲۷ and 742 is ۷۴۲. Which of these represents the number 247 ?

A ۴۷۲   B ۲۴۷   C ۷۲۴   D ۷۲۴   E ۷۴۲

P5 An extra large tub of mini-heroes chocolates weighs 1.5 kg including wrappings. The weight of the chocolates is 1.44 kg. How much do the wrappings weigh?

A 6 g   B 39 g   C 60 g   D 390 g   E 600 g

P6 A clock strikes only the hours. How many times does it strike altogether in twenty four hours?

A 24   B 48   C 78   D 156   E 312

Puzzling problems

P7 Each year on Maundy Thursday the queen gives away special coins called 'Maundy money'. This year she was 77 years old, so she gave 77 pence each to 77 men and 77 women. Approximately how much money was this altogether ?

    A £2   B £12   C £60   D £120   E £1200

P8 How wide is each of the shaded cushions on this sofa ?

    A 75 cm   B 85 cm   C 95 cm
    D 1 m 50 cm   E 1 m 70 cm

P9 What is the first prime number of the millennium?

    A 2001   B 2002   C 2003   D 2004   E 2005

P10 Sian thinks of a number. She multiplies it by 6 then adds 8. Finally she halves it and gets the answer 7. What number did she start with ?

    A 1   B $2\frac{1}{2}$ C 25   D 56   E 160

P11 Think of a positive number, multiply it by 5, add 1, double what you have, take away 2, and divide by the number you first thought of. What answer do you get?

    A 5   B 10   C 12   D 15   E can't tell

P12 If the 21st February 2004 is a Saturday, what day of the week will 2nd March be?

    A Sunday   B Monday   C Tuesday
        D Wednesday   E Saturday

P13 Which weighs the most?

    A 100 pennies   B 100 two pence pieces   C 100 five pence pieces
    D 100 20p bits   E 100 £2 coins

Puzzling problems

P14 I count down from 717 in sevens until I get a negative number. What is that negative number?

A −1   B −2   C −3   D −4   E −5

P15 Which of these fractions is nearest to a half ?

A $\dfrac{1}{3}$ B $\dfrac{3}{5}$ C $\dfrac{5}{7}$ D $\dfrac{7}{9}$ E $\dfrac{9}{11}$

P16 The diagram shows a crowd leaving a pop concert. The crowd divides equally at each split in the road. What fraction of the crowd goes down road X ?

A $\frac{1}{9}$ B $\frac{1}{6}$ C $\frac{1}{5}$ D $\frac{1}{4}$ E $\frac{2}{5}$

P17 Cindi has strands of beads in her hair. Half the strands have 2 beads, and half have 3 beads. If she has 90 beads, how many strands are in her hair?

A 15   B 18   C 36   D 45   E 90

P18 Jelly Beans cost 52 p, Pom Bom mints cost 12 p. Given £5, you want to buy the same number of each. What is the maximum number of sweets you can buy?

A 5   B 7   C 12   D 14   E 15

P19 Two people start running around an obstacle course. One takes six minutes to do one lap, the other eight minutes. How many times will the slower person go around the course before meeting up with the faster one?

A 3   B 4   C 6   D 8   E 24

Puzzling problems

P20 Where should I put the number 28 in this Venn diagram ?

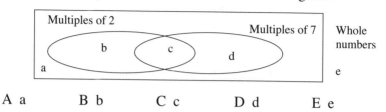

    A a   B b   C c   D d   E e

P21 In a class of 30 students at Cramem College (motto 'Usendem Wesortem'), only 6 remembered their pens and 8 remembered their diaries. Five students remembered both their pens and diaries. How many students forgot to bring both pens and diaries ?

    A 11   B 16   C 21   D 22   E 25

P22 Maud drew an isosceles triangle in which one of the (internal) angles was 120°. What were sizes of the other two angles?

    A each 30°   B 20° and 40°   C each 60°
    D 120° and 60°   E impossible to say

P23 Which can you NOT draw, going over each line only once and without taking your pencil off the paper?

P24 How many regular hexagons are in this diagram ?

    A 1   B 4   C 7   D 8   E 12

P25 I was facing East. I then turned 855° clockwise. In which direction am I now facing?

    A NE   B SE   C SW   D NW   E N

Puzzling problems

P26 Here are sketches of some triangles. Sam has marked the lengths in cm and the angles in degrees. He then tries to draw them accurately. How many are possible?

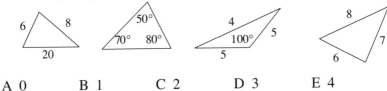

A 0   B 1   C 2   D 3   E 4

P27 Which of these statements is false ?

A All squares are rectangles   B All rectangles are parallelograms

C All rectangles are quadrilaterals

D All squares are quadrilaterals E All rectangles are squares

P28 How many parallelograms are there in this picture ?

A 1   B 9   C 10   D 36   E 40

P29 A 3 cm × 3 cm square is cut out of a 4 cm × 4 cm square of wood. How many cm² of wood remains?

A 1   B 7   C 9   D 16   E 25

P30 Which of these solids has three faces, two equal edges and no vertices ?

A cylinder   B cuboid   C sphere

D triangular prism   E cone

Puzzling problems

P31 Dr Doolittle's daughter has lots of pets. Skippy, her pet kangaroo, is twice as tall as she is. Porky, her pet pig, is half as tall as she is. Sylvester, her pet cat, is half as tall as Porky.
If Sylvester is 30 cm tall, how tall is Skippy ?

   A 15 cm   B 60 cm   C 1 m 20 cm
   D 2 m 40 cm   E 4 m 80 cm

P32 Doris has made a model of an octahedron. She wants to paint it so that no two faces that meet along an edge are the same colour. What is the least number of colours she needs to use ?

   A 1   B 2   C 4   D 6   E 8

P33 Five children took a test. There were 24 questions in the test and each child wrote down their score in a different way to impress their teacher.
Sally scored 19 marks.   Kamil got 75% of the questions correct.
Sam got 2/3 of the questions correct.
Pratima's ratio of correct answers to incorrect answers was 3:1.
Ryan got 1/8 of the questions wrong and the rest right.
Who scored the highest mark?

   A Sam   B Kamil   C Sally   D Pratima   E Ryan

P34 Phil McCann has a bucket under two leaks in his classroom roof. One leak drips at 4 ml per second and the other at 6 ml per second. His bucket leaks at 2 ml per second. How many seconds will it take to fill his 6000 ml bucket?

   A 500   B 750   C 1000   D 1500   E 3000

P35 Sixteen teams enter a knockout netball competition. In total how many games are needed to find the winner?

   A 8   B 12   C 15   D 16   E 64

Puzzling problems

P36 In a group of 14 boys, 7 have teddies and 5 have toy monkeys. What is the largest possible number of boys who have neither?

A none B 2   C 7   D 8   E 12

P37 A bag contains twelve toffees, eight mints, and four pieces of fudge. I pick out two sweets at random from the bag. What am I least likely to get?

A two pieces of fudge   B two mints   C two toffees
D two sweets that are the same   E it is not possible to find out.

P38 Five young people share a tent for five nights on a holiday. They all agree to say 'Goodnight' to everyone else in the tent every night. How many times is the word 'Goodnight' spoken on the holiday?

A 3   B 15   C 25   D 100   E 125

P39 My granny is more than 50 and less than 100 years old. She is 12 times my sister's age, 9 times my age and twice my mum's age. How old am I?

A 6   B 8   C 9   D 12   E 18

P40 Julie is thinking of a prime number which has two digits. If she turns the digits round she gets another prime number. Which of these numbers is she NOT thinking of?

A 13   B 17   C 19   D 37   E 79

P41 Mrs Multiple, the maths teacher, noticed that the reading on the milometer was 26962 miles. This is a palindromic number (it reads the same backwards as forwards). How many miles will she have to travel before the milometer displays the next palindromic number?

A 10   B 11   C 100   D 110   E 1110

Puzzling problems

P42 Patrick and 3 friends go into a shop at 9.17am to spend £1.23 on 3 packets of biscuits with 18 biscuits in each pack. He pays, getting 77p change and leaves the shop at 9.25am. The 4 boys eat 7 biscuits each. How long were the boys in the shop?

A £2   B 28 biscuits   C 12 min

D 41p each   E 8 min

P43 In our alphabet there are five vowels and twenty one consonants. Approximately what percentage of the letters in our alphabet are vowels?

A 5%   B 19%   C 21%   D 24%   E 26%

P44 Each time you flush the toilet, it uses 9 litres of water. An Olympic swimming pool holds two and a half million litres of water. About how many flushes would fill this pool?

A 278   B 2 778   C 27 778

D 277 778   E 2 777 778

P45 Crunch the cantankerous crocodile has a tail that is the same length as her head. Her body is twice the length of her tail. She measures 3m from nose to tail. How long is her tail?

A 50 cm   B 0.5 m   C 75 cm   D 1 m   E 1.5 m

P46 Rarry, Nermione, Hon and Heville each have a wand. Two of the wands measure 25 cm and two measure 20 cm. The children put them together, touching tips, on the table. Which of these shapes is impossible to make with these wands?

A rectangle   B arrowhead   C kite

D parallelogram   E square

Puzzling problems

P47 In a mathematical challenge, the first 20 questions are worth 1 mark each and the last 5 are worth 2 marks each. If you get exactly 15 questions right what is the most you could score?

A 15   B 20   C 25   D 30   E 35

P48 Maisie was telling me her mobile phone number but she sneezed in the middle. She said it was divisible by 9. I got her number as 07922?03441.
Which of these numbers could replace the unknown number?

A 0   B 1   C 2   D 3   E 4

P49 I have tables that seat 6 children, tables that seat 4 children and tables that seat 2 children.
What is the minimum number of tables I need to seat 79 children ?

A 12   B 13   C 14   D 16   E 18

P50 Rameses II ruled from 1279 BC to 1213 BC
Khufu ruled from 2551 BC to 2528 BC
Amenhotep III ruled from 1390 BC to 1352 BC
Hatschepsut ruled from 1479 BC to 1425 BC
Tutankhamun ruled from 1336 BC to 1328 BC
Which of these Egyptian Pharaohs ruled for the longest?

A Rameses II   B Khufu   C Amenhotep III
D Hatschepsut   E Tutankhamun

P51 I have six counters in the pattern shown.
The red is between the green and the blue.
The black is on the left. The green is above the black. The white is under the blue.
Where is the yellow counter?

A top left   B bottom middle   C bottom left
D top right   E bottom right

Puzzling problems

P52 Two cars make the same journey of 240 miles. One car does 40 miles per gallon (mpg) and the other 30 mpg. How many gallons of fuel are saved by using the first car?

A 2   B 6   C 8   D 10   E 14

P53 I go at 10 km per hour on my skateboard, and my friend travels at 8 km per hour on hers. In a one kilometre race, by how much time do I beat my friend?

A 1.5 min   B 2 min   C 2.5 min   D 6 min   E 7.5 min

P54 A train 200 m long enters a 1 km tunnel. It is travelling at 100 metres per second. How many seconds is it before the end of the train leaves the tunnel?

A 5   B 8   C 10   D 12   E 14

P55 In Roman numerals, I = 1, V = 5, X = 10 and L = 50 , so XXXV = 35. What is XXVII subtracted from LV ?

A XVI   B XVIII   C XXV   D XXVIII   E XXXIII

P56 Once every hour during lessons, my teacher says 'Nice joke, Sam, but settle down now'. We work in the classroom for five hours a day, 38 weeks of the year. How many times does she say this to Sam in a year ?

A 5   B 25   C 38   D 190   E 950

P57 ?thgie dna neves ,xis ,evif ,ruof fo naem eht si tahW

A evif tniop ruof B evif   C evif tniop evif
D xis   E neves

Puzzling problems

P58 A Hydra was a mythical creature with many heads. Every time a hero cut off one head, the Hydra would grow two more. If a Hydra started with nine heads, and the hero Mathematicus cut off three of them with his magical sword, how many heads would the Hydra then have once the new heads had grown?

A 6   B 12   C 15   D 18   E 21

P59 Jan and Kym are raising money for charity by collecting pennies and putting them end to end. So far they have one thousand pennies. Approximately how far does their line of pennies stretch?

A 1 m   B 2.1 m   C 21 m   D 100 m   E 210 m

P60 The Romans unit of weight, the *libra*, was about 327 grams. One twelfth of a *libra* was an *uncia*.
About how many grams were there in an *uncia* ?

A 12   B 20   C 24   D 27   E 30

Very challenging problems

V1 Work out three times a quarter of four times a third of 12.

    A 4   B 12   C 24   D 36   E 48

V2

What is the missing number?

5	67
9	8

4	59
9	7

4	52
7	?

    A 6   B 8   C 9   D 53   E 54

V3 I am a square number. The sum of my two digits is my square root. What number am I ?

    A 1   B 9   C 25   D 49   E 81

V4 172✪ is a 4-digit number but the last digit has been covered by a ✪. The number 172✪ is a multiple of three but not a multiple of two. What is the remainder when it is divided by 5?

    A 0   B 1   C 2   D 3   E 4

V5 What is the lowest prime number to be the sum of three different prime numbers?

    A 3   B 11   C 17   D 19   E 23

V6 a and b are two different whole numbers less than 10. If $a^3 = b^2$, what number could a be?

    A 2   B 3   C 4   D 5   E 8

V7 When 2^{100} is calculated, what is its last digit ?

    A 0   B 2   C 4   D 6   E 8

V8 A number that is equal to the sum of its factors apart from itself is called a perfect number. For example, the factors of 6 are 1, 2, 3 and 6 and $1 + 2 + 3 = 6$ so 6 is a perfect number. Which of these is a perfect number?

    A 25   B 26   C 27   D 28   E 29

Very challenging problems

V9 The ages of the three children in my family multiplied together come to 1001. How old is the oldest child?

A 7   B 11   C 13   D 17   E 19

V10 Illtyd tried to use a calculator to add two 2-digit numbers. But he pressed × instead of + and got the answer 325.
What was the correct answer to the addition?

A 25   B 32   C 38   D 70   E More information needed

V11   ☐ ☐ × ☐ ☐

I have four counters numbered 1, 2, 3 and 4. Using each counter only once, what is the largest number I can get if I make them into two 2-digit numbers and multiply them together?

A 312   B 1302   C 1312   D 1849   E 1936

V12 Which set of numbers gives a mean of 7, a median of 6 and a mode of 5 ?

A 4, 15, 5, 6, 6   B 5, 5, 7, 7, 11   C 4, 5, 6, 7, 8
D 7, 7, 7, 7, 7   E 7, 6, 5, 5, 12

V13 A set of four numbers has mode 7, median 10 and mean 15.
What is the range of the four numbers?

A 10   B 13   C 17   D 26   E more information is needed

V14 The diagram shows a black and white cubic liquorice allsort with three layers of equal thickness. What fraction of the outside is coloured black?

A $\dfrac{1}{3}$ B $\dfrac{2}{9}$ C $\dfrac{4}{15}$ D $\dfrac{1}{2}$ E $\dfrac{11}{15}$

V15 Which of these fractions gives 0.363636… when written as a decimal?

A $\dfrac{4}{10}$ B $\dfrac{4}{11}$ C $\dfrac{4}{12}$ D $\dfrac{4}{13}$ E $\dfrac{4}{14}$

Very challenging problems

V16 In an army, soldiers eat sandwiches made of square bread with sides ten centimetres. The officers have 5mm crust cut off all around the bread. What percentage of the area of bread is removed?

A 5 B 10 C 19 D 25 E 50

V17 Bob damaged his father's greenhouse with a football so his dad cut his pocket money by 20% until the new glass had been paid for. Bob has now paid off his debt. By how much should his dad increase his new pocket money to get back to its original amount ?

A 20% B 25% C 33% D 50% E 80%

V18 Jim, John and Jack have to share out some marbles.
The ratio of Jack's marbles to Jim's marbles is 1 : 4.
The ratio of Jim's marbles to John 's marbles is 2 : 3.
What is the ratio of John 's marbles to Jack's marbles?

A 1 : 2 B 3 : 1 C 1 : 6 D 6 : 1 E 1 : 8

V19 Dwight wants to make a huge chocolate cake for 27 people. The recipe for 3 people needs:
100 g margarine, 80 g sugar, 500 g flour and 65 g chocolate chips.
How many grams of sugar will he need?

A 7.20 B 710 C 720 D 780 E 860

V20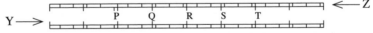

A train starts at Y travelling at 12 mph at the same time as a train from Z starts at 20 mph. They are travelling towards each other. Where do the trains cross?

A P B Q C R D S E T

Very challenging problems

V21 I cut a regular hexagon into two pieces. Which of these pairs of shapes is it not possible to get?

A two triangles   B two quadrilaterals   C a triangle and a pentagon
D a triangle and a heptagon   E a quadrilateral and a pentagon

V22 Each of the shapes below has width 8 cm and height 5cm. Which one has the largest perimeter?

A W   B X   C Y   D Z   E all the same

V23 A flag is in the shape of a rectangle. It is made up of five identical rectangles.
What is the area of the flag in m^2 ?

2.4m

A 2.4   B 4.8   C 7.2   D 9.6   E 14

V24 The diagram shows a square with a right-angled isosceles triangle on one side. The area of the triangle is 16 cm^2. What is the perimeter of the square in cm?

A 4   B 8   C 16   D 32   E 64

V25 On a can of paint is written '1 litre of paint will cover 10 m^2 of wall'. How many millimetres thick is the paint on the wall?

A too small to calculate   B 0.01 C 0.1   D 1   E 10

V26 In three-dimensional Noughts and Crosses, how many different ways are there which will give three noughts (or crosses) in a line?

A 24   B 39   C 45   D 48   E 49

Very challenging problems

V27 Which of these hollow shapes, when filled with water, would hold the most?

(Diagrams are not drawn to scale)

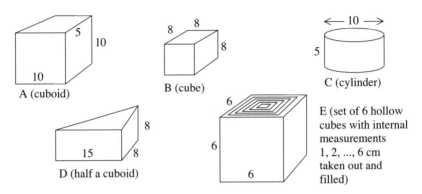

A (cuboid)

B (cube)

C (cylinder)

D (half a cuboid)

E (set of 6 hollow cubes with internal measurements 1, 2, ..., 6 cm taken out and filled)

V28 It takes 400g of plasticine to make a model of Big Ben.
I want to make a smaller scale model which is half as high.
How many grammes of plasticine will I need?

A 50   B 100   C 200   D 400   E 800

V29 A box whose shape is a cube with sides measuring
5cm is full. It contains 1 000 buttons. How many
identical buttons would be in a cubic box whose
sides measured 2.5cm each?

A 50   B 125   C 200   D 225   E 500

V30   pattern 1:   pattern 2: ⊞   pattern 3: ▦

The first pattern has 1 small square and 4 straight lines. The second
pattern gives 4 small squares and uses 6 straight lines. Continuing
this pattern, how many lines would be needed to draw 64 small
squares?

A 8   B 16   C 18   D 20   E 32

29

Very challenging problems

V31 This pattern has no lines of symmetry. What is the least number of extra squares that you would need to shade in to get a pattern with two lines of symmetry?

    A 2   B 3   C 4   D 5   E More than 5

V32 Violet is 150 cm tall. One sunny afternoon her shadow was 2 m long. Her father, who is 180 cm tall, was standing next to her. How long was his shadow?

    A 2 m   B 2.03 m   C 2.3 m   D 2.04 m   E 2.4 m

V33 Here is terrified Terry. His girlfriend Miss D Meanor says she can burst all 3 balloons with 3 arrows. The chance of each arrow bursting a balloon is $\frac{1}{2}$. What is the probability that all 3 balloons are burst with 3 arrows?

    A $\dfrac{1}{8}$ B $\dfrac{1}{4}$ C $\dfrac{1}{2}$ D 1   E $1\dfrac{1}{2}$

V34 At home I have Super Teddy who has lots of clothes: 2 shirts, 3 pairs of trousers and 4 hats.
How many different outfits can I dress Super Teddy in?

    A 1   B 3   C 9   D 12   E 24

V35 The security code number for the front door of Football College School is **1 9 6 6**. The door can, in fact, be opened by these four digits pressed in any order (e.g. 6 9 1 6).
How many different arrangements will allow access?

    A 4   B 10   C 12   D 16   E 24

V36 Balls are dropped from A and can fall down along the lines shown in this diagram. How many ways can the balls get from point A to point B?

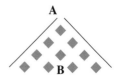

    A 1   B 2   C 4   D 6   E 8

Very challenging problems

V37 A 6-sided die has been weighted so that the probability of getting a six is $\frac{2}{5}$ and the probability of getting a one is $\frac{1}{10}$. If each of the other numbers is equally likely what is the probability of getting a 5?

A $\frac{1}{8}$ B $\frac{1}{7}$ C $\frac{1}{6}$ D $\frac{1}{5}$ E $\frac{1}{4}$

V38 There are two bags of balls. One has 12 blue balls, the other 12 red balls. I take half the blue balls and put them in the other bag. I shake this bag and take half of the balls and put them in the first bag. What fraction of the balls in the first bag are likely to be blue now?

A $\frac{1}{4}$ B $\frac{1}{2}$ C $\frac{3}{5}$ D $\frac{2}{3}$ E all of them

V39 My nephew is 2 years old. Which of these is closest to his age ?

A 1 000 000 seconds B 1 000 000 minutes C 1 000 000 hours
D 1 000 000 days E 1 000 000 weeks

V40 Mr and Mrs Diot and their son Ian were walking beside a river. Ian suddenly dived in. He swam at 4 mph, his body at right angles to the river bank. The river was flowing at 4 mph. At which point did he land on the other side of the river?

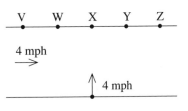

A V B W C X D Y E Z

V41 In four years time, I will be five times as old as I was sixteen years ago. How old am I?

A 21 B 22 C 25 D 26 E 27

V42 $F \times H = TK$ $\qquad K \times H = H$ $\qquad H \times H = RC$
These three multiplication facts are written in code. Each letter stands for the same digit all the time and different letters stand for different digits. Neither R nor T is 0. What does H stand for?

A 1 B 3 C 7 D 8 E 9

Very challenging problems

V43  I have a box of sweets. I eat one, then give two-thirds of the remainder to my brother and sister. Then I eat one, and give away two thirds again. Then I eat another one and give away two thirds of those remaining. I now have one left, which I eat! What is the smallest number of sweets that I could have started with?

A 27   B 30   C 31   D 39   E 40

V44 Diddiman School has less than 100 pupils. When the head teacher tried to line the pupils up in pairs little Kenny had no partner. She tried lining them up in threes but again Kenny was left on his own. She tried lining up in fours and finally in fives but each time Kenny was left out.
How many pupils were there in the school?

A 21   B 31   C 49   D 61   E 91

V45 Lisa had a set of little cubes that she made into one large cube. Bart knocked the large cube over and then the cat ate two of the small cubes. Then Bart rearranged the remaining little cubes into a square instead. How many cubes were there in each side of the square?

A 3   B 4   C 5   D 6   E 10

V46 Yen has six coins, one of each of the values 1p, 2p, 5p, 10p, 20p, 50p. How many totals below £1 can she not make using one or more coins? *(For example, 75p could be made with the 50p, 20p and 5p.)*

A 8   B 18   C 20   D 28   E 36

V47 2002 is a palindrome, which means it is the same backwards as forwards. The previous palindromic year was in 1991, 11 years before 2002. How many years will it be between 2002 and the next palindromic year?

A 10   B 11   C 101   D 110   E 1001

Very challenging problems

V48 There were 16 runners in the 800m final on Sports Day. I missed the finish so I asked six of my friends to tell me the number of the winner. These were their answers:

It was even   *It was odd*   *It was prime*
It was a square number *It had two digits*   *It was between 6 and 14*

Only FOUR of my friends had told the truth. Which number was the winner?

   A 5   B 9   C 11   D 12   E 16

V49 A recipe for chocolate chip cookies uses twice as much flour as butter. If I use 300 grams of flour and butter is sold in four ounce packets, how many packets of butter do I need?

   A 1   B 2   C 3   D 4   E 5

V50

One item of food FREE

Egg and chips £1.80   *Sausage, egg and chips £2.20*
Fish and chips £2.40   *Egg on toast £1.00*
Sausage and chips £1.20

Which meal is the café giving away for free?

   A egg   B chips   C fish   D sausage   E toast

V51 In a café, two samousas and three pakoras cost £3.10. But three samousas and two pakoras cost £2.90. What is the cost of one pakora?

   A 50p   B 58p   C 62p   D 70p   E £1.45

V52 Large balloons cost 30p each, and small balloons cost 13p each. I spend £3.57, and buy 17 balloons. How many large balloons do I get?

   A 7   B 8   C 9   D 10   E 11

V53 Yesterday I saw a whole lot of nanonits and nanognats. There were 150 legs altogether, and three more nanonits than nanognats. How many of these space creatures could there have been?

nanognat

   A 18   B 20   C 21   D 23   E 25

nanonit

Very challenging problems

V54 From my window I can see a park with dogs and people. There are 40 ears and 66 legs. How many people are there in the park?

A 7   B 10   C 13   D 20   E 33

V55 If each of the cubes in this solid measures 2 cm along each edge, what is the area of the surface of the solid?

A 18 cm² B 36 cm² C 72 cm² D 108 cm² E 144 cm²

V56 Sylvester and Sylvia are a pair of toads who have been catching flies. They told me that if Sylvester were to give half his flies to Sylvia, Sylvia would then have ten more than him. How many flies did Sylvia catch?

A 5   B 10   C 15   D 20   E 25

V57

At a funfair, people have three shots aiming at tin bunnies. If they hit a bunny, it stays down. The score is the total of the numbers on the bunnies you have hit. Which of these scores is impossible to get?

A 18   B 20   C 23   D 24   E 27

V58 At a fun fair, five tin bunnies in a circle go round and round, taking five seconds for each complete turn. An air rifle shoots every four seconds at this revolving target. The first shot hits bunny P. Which is the last bunny to be hit?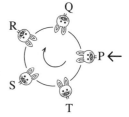

A P   B Q   C R   D S   E T

Very challenging problems

V59 Polly the pigeon, Charlie the cheetah, Harry the hare and Sally the snake agree to have a race. Maximum speeds are: pigeon 100 mph, cheetah 60 mph, hare 40 mph and a snake 10 mph. They start as shown in the diagram. Who wins?

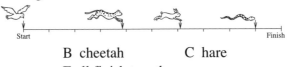

A pigeon   B cheetah   C hare
D snake   E all finish together

V60 My VCR (video) rewinds at eighteen cm per second. It takes nine cm of tape to record ten seconds of television. If I have recorded a twenty minute show of *The Simpsons,* how many minutes will it take the VCR to rewind the cassette?

A 1   B 2   C 5   D 6   E 10

V61 Three women, Delores, Lavinia and Paulette, were stuck in a lift during a heatwave. Delores had four bottles of mineral water with her and Lavinia had five. They shared the nine bottles of water equally between the three of them.

Once they had been freed, Paulette gave Delores and Lavinia nine coins as payment. What is the fairest method of dividing the nine coins?

	A	B	C	D	E
Delores:	3 coins	4 coins	5 coins	6 coins	7 coins
Lavinia:	6 coins	5 coins	4 coins	3 coins	2 coins

V62 Hungry Henrietta has a chocolate machine which makes chocolates at 10 per minute. She eats them at 20 per minute. She has 100 ready at the start. If she eats all the chocolates, approximately how long is it before she runs out?

A 2 min   B 5 min   C 10 min   D 20 min   E never

V63 My dog Dougal eats exactly three tins of food every four days. We are going away for two weeks. What is the smallest number of tins of food we must leave for the dog-sitter?

A 10   B 11   C 12   D 13   E 14

Very challenging problems

V64 I have two dogs who eat the same dog food. I have ten tins of dog food. Gnasher eats a tin of food in two days; Nibbles eats a tin of food in five days. What is the latest day on which I must buy some more tins of dog food?

    A 1st   B 7th   C 10th   D 15th   E 16th

V65 The world record for domino toppling was set in 2003 by a Chinese woman who spent 13 hours a day for 45 days setting up 303 628 dominoes in a line approximately 15 km long. The last seven dominoes did not fall but she still beat the previous record of 281 581. On average how many dominoes did she set up each hour?

    A 20   B 50   C 200   D 500   E 1000

V66 Mathematicus, the unbeatable Gladiator of Ancient Rome, fights three different opponents each day for five days. He receives two and a half silver pieces for each fight. If he needs 50 silver pieces to buy his freedom, how many *more* fights at the same rate of pay would he have to win?

    A 3   B 5   C 7   D 8   E 12

V67 One day Addum is infected with a mathematical virus. People with this virus infect three other people the next day but then do not infect any more people. How many days after Addum was infected will it take to infect a thousand people with the virus originating from Addum?

    A 3   B 4   C 5   D 6   E 7

Easy problems – Answers and Notes

E1 C 6

There are six tadpoles.

E2 C 1

Your pupils could try a similar sum but with numbers, like this:
$$1 - 1 + 1 - 1 + \ldots + 1.$$

E3 C 10

Easy to add up this sum. Try $1 + 2 + 3 + \ldots + 9 + 10$.

E4 D 1234

Setting this sum out correctly will give 1234. Alternatively, pupils might notice there are four units, three tens, etc. Does this pattern continue indefinitely?

E5 C 8

$2 \times 2 \times 2 = 8$.

E6 E 7 × 7

E7 B 6 & 30

Pupils will be used to tables like this!

E8 B 2

$\frac{3}{4}$ and $\frac{7}{8}$ are greater than $\frac{1}{2}$.

E9 B $\frac{1}{4}$

$\frac{1}{2} = \frac{2}{4}$ so half of two quarters is $\frac{1}{4}$.

E10 C $\frac{5}{6}$

Keep going with this series of fractions and they get closer to 1!

E11 C $\frac{5}{8}$

Drawing in a diagonal across the lower right square will give 8 equal triangles in the diagram. So the shaded area is $\frac{5}{8}$.

Easy problems – Answers and Notes

E12 E   607 203

Pupils need to understand place value to get this one correct.

E13 C   42

The rule is 'add the previous two numbers'.

E14 E   55

A 54   B 50   C 53   D 53   E 55

E15 C   8

Some pupils might list and count the multiples, but others might think '8 fives are 40, so there are 8 multiples'.

E16 D   5 years

A five week old cat is not yet adult. So the answer is five years. What would be the answer if I were a mouse, or a quickly-growing bacteria?

E17 C   parallelogram

E18 D

The other shapes are circle, kite, polygon and triangle.

E19 E

Hexagons have six straight sides.

E20 B   N, E, S

To escape you must go north, then east, then south. Can your pupils draw a maze which needs certain directions to escape? Try N, S, E, W.

E21 E

All have an area of four small squares except E which has five.

Easy problems – Answers and Notes

E22 E △

Looking at the end of the prism would give a triangle.
Drawing front and side elevations and plans for different shapes
provides an understanding of 3-D figures. Try using an OHP
with solid shapes and looking at the shadow.

E23 B **semicircle**

If the goat pulls the rope taut and walks, it will move in a
semicircle.   Pupils could tie up Billy against differently-shaped
walls, for example, on a short wall, on the corner of a building,
or in the centre of a field with an open gate on one side.
Intelligent goats could follow a mathematical rule: no rope but
promising to stay the same distance from two apple trees!

E24 A $\frac{1}{4}$

Adding the two lines of symmetry gives eight equal triangles; 2
out of 8 have been shaded.

E25 A **15**

There are six cubes each side and three on top makes 15.
Or there are five cubes in front, five in the middle and five at the
back.
Several (similar) approaches can be used to solve problems like
this. Some pupils can get real satisfaction in using different
methods and getting the same answer each time. Two methods
for solving this problem are given above. A third would be to say
the cuboid has $3 \times 3 \times 2 = 18$ cubes, less the three making the
hole. The volume problem shown here can be solved in three
different ways.

E26 A ∀ΓICE

This is not as easy as it looks! A mirror above A gives the word
ALICE.
Pupils could put a mirror in different positions and draw
different images of the word ALICE (the name of the daughter
of a PMC Problems Team member).

Easy problems – Answers and Notes

E27 B 2 metres

A door is about two metre rules high, or just bigger than 6 ft. i.e. 2 m.

E28 A 487

There are many ways of calculating 1000 − 513. One way (provided by a pupil in a PMC school) is 'take one off 1000', calculate 999 − 513 (no 'borrowing' needed), then replace the one.

E29 C 25

10 metres in 2 hours means 5 metres in one hour; so in 5 hours the snail would travel 25 metres. By ratios, the distance travelled is 10 × (5 ÷ 2) = 25.

E30 D 50

5 × 10

E31 A 1992

Subtraction: 2003 − 11 = 1992.

E32 E 60

There will be 5 × 12 pence in five shillings.

E33 A 50 minutes

Most pupils will probably add the 10 minutes to 5pm to the 40 minutes after 5pm to give 50 min.

E34 A 4p

5 on its own, 1 + 5 = 6, 2 × 5 = 7 and 1 + 2 + 5 = 8 but Max cannot make 4p.

If Max now had a 10p coin as well as the other coins, what sums of money up to 18p could he not make? (4p, 9p and 14p.) And with a 20p coin as well? What is the minimum number of coins needed to make all amounts of money up to £1?

Harder problems – Answers and Notes

H1   B   13 212

The calculation is $12000 + 1200 + 12$.

H2   A   111 111 111

Multiplying the units gives $9 \times 9 = 81$, ending in 1. So …!
Pupils could try $12\,345\,679 \times 18$ or by 27 or any multiple of 9.
When does this pattern break down?

H3   E $2^2 \div 2^2$

$1^2 + 1^2 = 2$; $1^2 - 1^2 = 0$; $2^2 - 1^2 = 3$; $3^2 - 2^2 = 5$ and
$2^2 \div 2^2 = 1$.
How can the answer 4 be achieved using squares?
How can the answer 1 be achieved using cubed numbers?

H4   D   9

$0^5 = 0$, $1^4 = 1$, $2^3 = 8$, $3^2 = 9$, and $4^1 = 4$. So 3^2 is the
largest.
If the pattern in the problem were continued, the next expression
would be 5^0. Most pupils would say this must
have a value zero. But if they work through the pattern
5^3, 5^2, 5^1, 5^0 they might get to $5^0 = 1$.
Pupils could try this pattern and see what they find:
$$2^4 = \quad, 2^3 = \quad, 2^2 = \quad, 2^1 = \quad, 2^0 = \quad, 2^{-1} = \quad, 2^{-2} =$$

H5   E   8000

There are 8000 halves in 4000. Pupils could use fraction rules to
calculate this. Alternatively, $4000 \div \frac{1}{2}$ is equal to 4000×2.

H6   C   2

$\frac{1}{2} + \frac{1}{2} = 1$; $\frac{1}{2} - \frac{1}{2} = 0$; $\frac{1}{2} \times \frac{1}{2} = \frac{1}{4}$ and $\frac{1}{2} \div \frac{1}{2} = 1$.
The problem in the challenge uses two halves. Here is a
different problem. How many different numbers can you make
using four halves and the usual mathematical operation symbols?
Can your pupils make 0, $\frac{1}{2}$, 1, $1\frac{1}{2}$, 2, 3. How about $-\frac{1}{4}$? Any
others?

Harder problems – Answers and Notes

H7 C 375

Half of 1500 is 750 and half of 750 is 375.

H8 B $\frac{3}{8}$

After eating half, half is left; i.e. $\frac{4}{8}$ is left. $\frac{1}{8}$ is given to a friend leaving $\frac{3}{8}$.

H9 E 11

2, 3 and 5 can easily be seen to be factors. 101010 is divisible by 7 but not 11.

H10 D 5

2004 does not end in a 5 or 0 so 5 is not a factor.
Pupils could list all the factors of 2004: 1, 2, 3, 4, 6, 12, 167, 334, 501, 668, 1002, 2004.

H11 C 25

$2005 = 5 \times 401$. So 5 is a factor, but 25 is not.
The numbers 2000 to 2005 provide an interesting range of factors: $2000 = 24 \times 53$, $2001 = 3 \times 23 \times 29$, $2002 = 2 \times 7 \times 11 \times 13$, 2003 is prime, $2004 = 22 \times 3 \times 167$ and $2005 = 5 \times 401$.

H12 B 13

13 is a prime number and so would need a long thin pack.
What number less than 30 gives the largest number of ways of packing pills in rectangular arrays?
(24, which is 2×12, 3×8 and 4×6)

H13 D 30

30 is the only number which is an even number, a multiple of 3 and a multiple of 5.

H14 D 4

1, 4, 9 and 16 are the square numbers between 0 and 20.

Harder problems – Answers and Notes

H15 E **all square**

The numbers are not all odd, less than 625, prime or numbers divisible by 3. So, by default, they must be square numbers. In fact they are 8^2, 11^2, 17^2 and 25^2.

Pupils could be asked to find numbers which are:

a) odd and also prime   b) odd and also divisible by 3

c) odd and square   d) prime and divisible by 3 (!?!)   e) square and divisible by 3.

H16 B **12 × 3**

The words *share*, *take* and *altogether* may confuse pupils but 12 children each have 3 biscuits so the calculation is 12×3.

Pupils could make up stories which use calculations such as $12 + 3$ and 12×3.

H17 C **72 × 5**

Pupils might work out $5 \times 8 \times 9 = 360$, and then choose the suggested answers to find the one which is also 360. But it saves brain-ache to match them to $5 \times 8 \times 9$. It is 72×5 that has the same value as $5 \times 8 \times 9$.

Looking at $5 \times 8 \times 9$, pupils could be asked to list pairs of numbers which have the same value; i.e. 40×9, 45×8 and 5×72.

H18 C **7.15**

H19 E

The only correct clock after rotation is E.

H20 D **pentagon**

This is quite hard to imagine but a folded rectangle will show the pentagon clearly.

H21 D $\frac{1}{2}$

Mark in the centre of the hexagon and join it to the corners of the black triangle. All six triangles now shown are congruent and are equal in area.

Harder problems – Answers and Notes

H22 E circle

The sides of the square are straight and so a circle is not possible.
Pupils can use a square piece of paper and see how many shapes
they can make with one fold, two folds etc.

H23 D 13

Try drawing triangles with sides 5, 5 and 13; and 5, 7 and 13! A
5, 13, 13 triangle is isosceles.

Pupils can work through the possibilities provided by the
question and answers, discovering which arrangements are
impossible to draw. Here is another impossible shape: draw a
triangle with sides of length 7 cm, 7 cm and 14 cm. Is there a
rule for checking if a triangle with three known sides can be
drawn?

H24 B 10 cm

$10 \times 10 = 100$, or the square root of 100 is 10.

H25 A 5 cm

There are 8 sectors in the web ($360 \div 45$) so the distance
travelled is one eighth of 40 cm.

H26 B 20

The original large cube had 27 small cubes, but 7 have been
removed.

Alternatively, there are 8 in the top layer, 8 in the bottom layer
and 4 in the middle, making a total of 20 cubes.

H27 A

All these 3-D shapes will tessellate except for the curved shape.
It is hard to make enough of these shapes to show a 3-D
tessellation. But pupils could verify that they tessellate
by explaining how they would fit together.

H28 B 2

There are no vertical or horizontal lines of symmetry but the two
diagonals are lines of symmetry.

Harder problems – Answers and Notes

H29 D 8

The letters which have at least one line of symmetry are M, E, A, U, E, M, E and T. That is eight letters.

H30 C 22

One-fifth of 55 is 11, so two-fifths is 22.

H31 D £15

Colin gets £5 a week and receives a quarter of the 'pie'. So Peter and Ruth together receive three times £5 which is £15.

H32 D 5 for the price of 3

Responses C and E are very silly! A offers 3 for 100p (33p each); B offers 5 for 200p (40p each); D offers 5 for 150p (30p each). So D offers the best value.

H33 C 3 for 26p

The price in pence per teddy is: A 10 p   B 9 p   C $8\frac{2}{3}$p   D $8\frac{3}{4}$ p   E $8\frac{4}{5}$p. So the cheapest is C ($8\frac{2}{3}$ p).
Pupils could work on their own 'best value' for prices in shops.

H34 D 10.48

At 10 mph, Lee would take a fifth of an hour (12 minutes) to cycle 2 miles. So he started out at 10.48.

H35 C 280

$35 \times 8 = 280$ miles.

H36 D 45

If three Googleblips have 27 tentacles, then one Googleblip has 9 tentacles. So five Googleblips have 45 tentacles.

H37 D 24

Each of these sloths have 12 toes so there are 24 on two sloths. Lime's two-toed sloths have two toes on the front and three on the back. How many toes are there on two of these sloths?

Harder problems – Answers and Notes

H38 C 5 pm

Total time taken is 30 + 15 + 5 = 50 min.

H39 C £5.39

Multiplication: 7 × 77 p = £5.39.

H40 C 9

'All but nine died' means nine still live.

H41 D 10 hr 46 min

My main sleep lasts 9 hr 50 min then I doze for 56 min.

H42 C 6 and 9

Checking through the possible answers gives 6 and 9 as the only pair that add to 15 and multiply to 54.

H43 E 3 hr 20 min

Dina will take 200 minutes to drink 100 bottles. This is 3 hr 20 min.

H44 D Sunday

Today must be Friday so the day after tomorrow is Sunday. Can the pupils make up other similar questions?

H45 D 41

Freda: 4 fish every 5 minutes so 16 fish every 20 minutes;
Fred: 5 fish every 4 minutes so 25 fish every 20 minutes.
So a total of 41 fish would be fried in twenty minutes.

H46 C 25

In 30 minutes, Tim ties 45 twigs and Tom ties 20 twigs.
So Tim ties 25 more twigs than Tom.

H47 D 600

Feeding time is three times a day on four days each week; i.e. 12 treats of 50 peanuts; that is 12 × 50 = 600 peanuts for each week.

Harder problems – Answers and Notes

H48 D 2

The calculation is $5 - 9 + 6 = 2$.

In mathematics we can wander into worlds which are different to ours. We could have a world with fractional numbers of people, negative money (is this our world?) or 4-D space. Once, travel was in two dimensions; now it is in three. Pupils can play O's and X's in 2-D. Can they play it in 3-D, or even 4-D? Pupils could write some problems about imaginary worlds.

H49 E 24

Each page, when folded in half, will make 4 pages: $4 \times 6 = 24$. Problems on pages of booklets can get more complicated. In a 24-page booklet made of 6 sheets of paper folded in half, what page would be printed beside page 3 if the booklet was taken apart? There is a rule here!

H50 C 40p

There are several ways of solving this problem. Firstly, test the possible answers. Secondly, £1.20 ÷ 3 = 40 p; by symmetry the 10p up and 10p down cancel each other out. Thirdly, the equation $a + 10 + a + a - 10 = 120$ gives $a = 40$.

H51 B very unlikely

It couldn't be you if a win were impossible! The slogans for the National Lottery have changed from 'It could be you' to 'Maybe just maybe' to 'Don't live a little, live a Lotto' deflecting players from the chances of winning.

Pupils can get lottery probability information from shops which sell lottery tickets.

H52 E YXWVZ

People have different lifestyles but there are limits!
Pupils could plan their own activities, such as getting dressed or making a cake.

Harder problems – Answers and Notes

H53 C 10

Pupils will probably use a guess and check method. The numbers are 10 and 4.

H54 B 20

3×4 gives 12. So 4 and 5 are multiplied to give 20.

This question uses multiplication. Obviously, addition, subtraction and division could be used in similar problems. So too could more complex functions such as calculating the mean, and adding squares.

Here are a few suggestions:

a) 3 and 4 are to 7 as 4 and 5 are to ?   (9)

b) 3 and 4 are to 0.75 as 4 and 5 are to ?   (0.8)

c) 3 and 4 are to 25 as 4 and 5 are to ?   (41)

Puzzling problems – Answers and Notes

P1   E

Jamal missed out a decimal point and input 12.7 + 385.

P2   E   1300

There are 65 rows of 20 plants. Pupils will probably use mental arithmetic to work out 65 × 2 and then 'add a nought'.

P3   A   J and M

The diagram shows who dislikes whom!
So J and M do not dislike each other.

P4   B   ۲۴۷

۴ represents 4, ۲ is 2 and ۷ is 7. So 247 is ۲۴۷.
Some of your pupils may know of different scripts? Are they similar to the script we usually use?

P5   C   60 g

Using grams, the wrappings weigh 1500 − 1440 = 60 g.

P6   D   156

1 + 2 + 3 + ... + 12 = 78. Doubling gives 156.
Pupils could try adding 1, 2, 3, ... 12 by linking 1 with 12, 2 with 11 and thereby getting 6 × 13 = 78.
What is 1 + 2 + 3 + ... + 100 ? (50 × 101 = 5050)

P7   D   £120

The queen will give 77 × 77p to the men and 77 × 77p to the women. That is 2 × £59.29 = £118.58 (£120). As an approximate answer is required, pupils could think of 80p given to 80 men and 80 women, giving 2 × 80 × 80 = £128.

P8   A   75 cm

1 m 90 cm − 40 cm = 1 m 50 cm. Dividing by two gives 75 cm.

Puzzling problems – Answers and Notes

P9   C   2003

2002 and 2004 are divisible by 2. 2001 (and 2004) are divisible by 3. 2005 is divisible by 5. That leaves 2003 which is not divisible by any number except one and itself.

After 2003, what are the next few prime numbers?

What strategies can your pupils use? They could create an 'Eratosthenes Sieve' starting with 2001, crossing out multiples of 2, 3, 5, 7 etc. using prime numbers up to 43. That is hard! Perhaps it would be simpler to check each number by itself! (The next two are 2011 and 2017.)

P10   A   1

Some pupils will select the answers and try them out.

Again, pupils might work this problem in reverse, using inverses; i.e. double 7, subtract 8 and divide by 6.

P11   B   10

Start with 1: $1 \to 5 \to 6 \to 12 \to 10 \to 10$.
Start with 2: $2 \to 10 \to 11 \to 22 \to 20 \to 10$.
Start with x: $x \to 5x \to 5x + 1 \to 10x + 2 \to 10x \to 10$.
Pupils can design their own puzzles which will produce a fixed end number if they follow the correct rules! Algebra can prove the answer.

P12   C   Tuesday

2004 is a leap year so there are 29 days in February.

P13   E   100 £2 coins

We are comparing 100 of each kind of coin. The £2 coins are the heaviest.

Practical problems: How much do 100 pennies weigh compared to a £1? Which coins together are closest in weight to their comparative values? For example, do two 50p coins weigh the same as a £1 coin?

Puzzling problems – Answers and Notes

P14 D −4

Subtracting $102 \times 7 (= 714)$ leaves 3. Taking away 7 gives −4.

There are other examples of problems in which remainders are important. Here are two.

If today is a Tuesday, what day of the week will it be in 100 days from now? I have 100 eggs; if I want to fill small egg boxes (6 eggs), how many eggs will I have left over?

P15 B $\frac{3}{5}$

The fractions are increasing in value so $\frac{5}{7}$, $\frac{7}{9}$ and $\frac{9}{11}$ can be ruled out as they are larger in value than $\frac{3}{5}$.

$\frac{1}{3} = \frac{10}{30}$; $\frac{3}{5} = \frac{10}{30}$. $\frac{18}{30}$ is nearer to $\frac{15}{30}$ than $\frac{10}{30}$. So $\frac{3}{5}$ is nearest to $\frac{1}{2}$.

P16 B $\frac{1}{6}$

Half the crowd turn left at the first junction which then splits into three roads. A third of a half is one sixth.

Pupils could work out the fractions for the other roads. The total of all four fractions should be 1. Can pupils design different road systems which can allow these fractions of a crowd travelling down a road? $\frac{1}{8}$, $\frac{1}{7}$, $\frac{3}{4}$.

P17 C 36

Imagine a pair of strands, taking together a 2-bead and a 3-bead strand. $90 \div 5$ gives 18 pairs of strands; i.e. 36 individual strands.

P18 D 14

We want to buy the same number of each, so one Jelly Bean and one Pom Bom costs $52 + 12 = 64$p.

$500\text{p} \div 64\text{p} = 7.8$ approx. So 14 sweets can be bought.

Suppose there were twice as many mints as beans?

Or one more mint than beans?

Puzzling problems – Answers and Notes

P19 A   3

This problem can seem really difficult. Pupils can draw
diagrams showing where the faster and slower athletes are after
6, 12, 18 and 24 minutes. It becomes clear that the slower
athlete is first lapped after 24 minutes. In this time the slower
athlete has gone around the obstacle course 3 times. The LCM of
6 and 8 is 24 and $24 \div 8 = 3$.

Using different numbers in the problems will provide practice in
using LCMs.

P20 C   c

28 is a multiple of both 2 and 7 and will go in the space marked
c.

P21 C   21

Solving this problem can be muddling but using a Venn diagram
makes it easy. You can provide similar problems which can be
solved by the use of Venn diagram. Here are four.

In the class of 30 pupils at Cramem College, how many forgot to
bring both pens and diaries when ....

a)   16 remembered pens, 18 remembered diaries,
     5 remembered both? (Ans. 1)
b)   15 remembered pens, 18 remembered diaries,
     3 remembered both? (Ans. 0)
c)   13 remembered pens, 14 remembered diaries,
     13 remembered both? (Ans. 16)
d)   15 remembered pens, 17 remembered diaries,
     0 remembered both? (Ans. -2 !)

P22 A   each 30°

An isosceles has two equal angles; the angles of the triangle add
up to 180°. So each of the two unknown angles must be 30°.
There is only one possibility for an isosceles triangle with one
angle of 120°. But can your pupils find two different
possibilities for an isosceles triangle with an angle of 50°? (50°,
50° and 80°; and 50°, 65° and 65°.)

52

Puzzling problems – Answers and Notes

P23 E

You have to choose your starting point carefully, but all, except E, can be drawn according to the rules.

An analysis of the 'junctions' helps. If there are more than two odd junctions (i.e. 3, 5, 7, etc lines out) it is not possible to draw with these rules. All these drawings have two three-lined junctions except E which has four.

Pupils could make up other possible and impossible designs.

P24 D 8

There are eight hexagons, seven small and one large.

The diagram in the PMC paper shows a hexagon with sides of two units. A hexagon of side one unit obviously contains one hexagon. The hexagon in the paper contains 8 hexagons. Pupils can draw larger hexagons to spot the pattern. The number of hexagons contained is the sequence of cube numbers (1, 8, 27, 64 ...).

A very interesting pattern can be found by tabling the number of differently-sized hexagons in these increasing patterns. In fact the numbers 1, 7, 19, 37 ... are the number of dots inside the hexagons!

P25 C SW

A complete rotation is 360° and two of these will give a remaining 135°. This is 90° plus 45° so I will end up facing south west.

P26 B 1

The first triangle fails the $a + b < c$ rule. In the second, the sum of the angles is not 180°. In the third, the side opposite the 100° angle should be the largest side but it isn't! The last triangle is the only one which can be accurately drawn.

Pupils could try to draw these triangles. Can they think of other triangles or other shapes that are impossible to draw? Maybe a quadrilateral with sides 3 cm, 4 cm, 5 cm and 12 cm!) Thinking of other misleading triangles: how many triangles can be drawn with two sides 10 cm and 8 cm and with one angle 50° ?

Puzzling problems – Answers and Notes

P27 E

All statements are true except '*All rectangles are squares*'.
Pupils could make up more statements about geometric shapes
which are either true or false! For example 'Are triangles
quadrilaterals with one side of length zero?'

P28 D 36

The parallelograms are 9 (1 by 1), 4 (2 by 2), 1 (3 by 3),
3 (3 by 1), 3 (1 by 3), 6 (2 by 1), 6 (1 by 2), 2 (3 by 2), 2 (2 by 3).
If the shapes were all rectangles and you were counting
rectangles, would there be a different answer? No. Rhombi?
Yes, 14. Squares? 14.

P29 B 7

$(16 - 9)$ cm^2 = 7 cm^2.

P30 A cylinder

The cylinder is the only solid listed with no vertex, so cylinder is
the answer. Members of the PMC Problems Team had a long
discussion on the notion of curved faces. Your comments on this
are welcome!

P31 D 2 m 40 cm

If Sylvester is 30 cm tall, Porky is 60 cm tall, the daughter is 120
cm tall so Skippy is 2 m 40 cm tall.
How would your pupils set about finding the height of a
kangaroo (or any other animal or object) that you could not
touch or reach?

P32 B 2

Faces of the same colour can meet at a vertex but not along an
edge. It is possible to use only 2 colours.

P33 E Ryan

Turning all the scores into marks out of 24 gives:

Sally 19;   Kamil 18;   Sam 16;   Ryan 21;   Pratima 18.

Puzzling problems – Answers and Notes

P34 B 750

The bucket takes in 10 ml per sec but loses 2 ml per sec, leaving 8 ml in the bucket each second. It will fill in
$600 \div 8 = 750$ (seconds).

How often would Phil McCann have to empty the bucket during a 2 hour maths lesson?

What happens if the bucket leaks at 12 ml per second?

P35 C 15

Eight games are needed in the first round, then four in the second round, then two in the semi-finals, then the finals, totalling 15.
Pupils could calculate the number of games needed for 8 teams in the knockout competition, then 32 and 64 teams. There is a pattern in the answers. Suppose there are more difficult numbers of teams (i.e. not a power of two), can the number of games needed be calculated using a formula?

But a much shorter approach altogther is to say that each game knocks out (eliminates) one team, so 15 games must be needed.

P36 C 7

To get the largest number who have neither, we can imagine the largest who have both (5). Two have only teddies, leaving seven who have neither. A Venn diagram may help describe the sets.

P37 A two pieces of fudge

It is possible to calculate the probabilities therefore E is incorrect. The probability of selecting two pieces of fudge is smaller than two mints or two toffees and certainly less likely than two sweets of any kind. So the answer is two pieces of fudge.

P(2 pieces of fudge) $= \frac{4}{24} \times \frac{3}{23} = \frac{12}{24 \times 23}$

P(2 mints) $= \frac{8}{24} \times \frac{7}{23} = \frac{56}{24 \times 23}$

P(2 toffees) $= \frac{12}{24} \times \frac{11}{23} = \frac{132}{24 \times 23}$

P(two of any kind) = the sum of the above three $= \frac{200}{24 \times 23}$.

Only a few pupils will have worked on calculating combined probabilities. Here is a simple example: My young brother always carries some milk and eggs from the shop. He drops the eggs 4 days out of 7 in any week, and he drops the milk on 3 days out of seven.

Puzzling problems – Answers and Notes

Pupils could try to calculate the probabilities of all the outcomes in this situation and check that they add up to one. Drawing a probability grid will help.

P38 D 100

Each night 5 people say 'Goodnight' to four others, making 20 'Goodnight's. So during five nights, there are $5 \times 20 = 100$ 'Goodnight's spoken.

The formula for calculating the number of 'Goodnight's for one night is $n(n-1)$. A similar problem uses the context of sending Christmas cards to each other.

Slightly harder, the number of diagonals in a polygon and the number of handshakes requires division by two i.e. $n(n-1) \div 2$. Why?

P39 B 8

The age of the granny is divisible by 12, 9 (and 2). The only possibility $(50 < g < 100)$ is 72. So I am $72 \div 9 = 8$ years old. Suppose granny is still between 50 and 100 years old and we ignore mother's age. We want to calculate my age. How many answers are there to these situations?

(a) She is six times my sister's age and nine times my age. How old am I?

(b) She is ten times my sister's age and twelve times my age. How old am I?

(c) She is seven times my sister's age and fifteen times my age. How old am I?

P40 C 19

The only number which, when written in reverse, does not give a prime number is 19 $(91 = 7 \times 13)$.

Can pupils find some facts about two-digit prime numbers which produce primes when the digits are reversed? (no even numbers allowed ...)

Puzzling problems – Answers and Notes

P41 D   110

Pupils could add the suggested answers to 26962 and look for a palindromic number. The next one is 27072.

P42 E   8 min

Pupils have to select the information they need to answer the question! They went into the shop at 9.17am and left at 9.25am so they were in the shop for 8 minutes.

There are other questions which could have been asked of the first three sentences. What are they? The first three sentences contain 9 numbers. Can your pupils get more than nine numbers in four sentences?

P43 B   19%

The percentage of letters which are vowels is $\frac{5}{26} \times 100$.
$\frac{5}{25}$ is a fifth i.e. 20%, so $\frac{5}{26}$ will be a little less, i.e. about 19%.

P44 D   277 778

Careful division by 9 needed here.
2 500 000 ÷ 9 = 277 778 (to the nearest flush!)

P45 C   75 cm

This is muddling! Her tail, head and two body lengths make four equal parts. $\frac{1}{4}$ of 3 m is 75 cm.

P46 E   square

All shapes can be made except a square. The four wands are not equal in length.

P47 B   20

In getting maximum marks, a pupil must get the last five questions correct. So this pupil will get 10 problems worth one mark each and 5 problems worth two marks each;
i.e. 10 + 10 = 20 marks.

Puzzling problems – Answers and Notes

P48 E 4

To be divisible by 9, the digits must add up to a multiple of 9. The digits we can see add up to 32. So the missing digit must be 4.
Can your pupils think of phone numbers with a missing (sneeze) digit which are divisible by 9 and which have two possible unknown digits? Can they find or justify any other rules for divisibility of numbers?

P49 C 14

Using the largest tables will give the minimum number of tables needed. So since 79 ÷ 6 = 13.166, we cannot manage with 13 tables so 14 tables are required.
Suppose there are 89 children. What tables should be chosen to minimise the number of spare seats?

P50 A Rameses II

Rameses II ruled for 66 years. The lengths of the reigns of the other Pharaohs are: Khufu 23 years, Amenhotep III 38 years, Hatschepsut 54 years and Tutankhamun 8 years.

P51 B bottom middle

Black is on the left and green is above the black; red is between the green and blue (so red is on the right top).
White is under the blue (right bottom) so the yellow is middle bottom!

P52 A 2

The first car uses 6 gallons, the second uses 8 gallons, saving 2 gallons.
On longer journeys the saving in fuel is obviously greater. Pupils could compare the fuel used by same two cars on a year's motoring of 12 000 miles, or in a lifetime.

P53 A 1.5 min

I take one tenth of an hour (6 min) and my friend takes one eighth of an hour ($7\frac{1}{2}$ min) so I win by $1\frac{1}{2}$ min.

Puzzling problems – Answers and Notes

P54 D   12

The distance travelled by the front of the train is 1200 m.

At 100 metres per second, this will take 12 seconds.

P55 D   XXVIII

LV = 55, and XXVII = 27. So the answer is 55 − 27 = 28.

It is possible to do it by decomposition, which is the 'Roman' way:

$$XXXXVVIIIII - XXVII = XXVIII$$

Poor Romans! Their method of displaying numbers was good in many ways, but ask your pupils to compare these calculations in our Arabic notation and in the Roman notation:

$$100 - 1, \qquad 23 \times 6, \qquad 49 \times 4.$$

P56 E   950

The teacher speaks to Sam $5 \times 5 (= 25)$ time each week; that is 25×38 times a year. This is approximately 1000, so the answer is 950.

P57 D   xis

This question has been printed backwards! It is a straightforward problem on means:

$$\frac{4 + 5 + 6 + 7 + 8}{5} = 6.$$

P58 B   12

The Hydra starts with 9 heads; 3 are cut off but six new heads grow. So there are now 12 heads.

P59 C   21 m

Pupils will have to estimate the diameter of a penny, which is about 2 cm. 1000×2 cm gives 2000 cm which is 20 m.

21 m is the nearest answer offered.

Pupils could estimate and then measure the width of their thumb for future use in estimating small distances like the diameter of a coin.

P60 D   about 27 g

$327 \div 12 = 27.25$. Estimating the answer is difficult.

Very challenging problems – Answers and Notes

V1 B 12

Working backwards: a third of 12 = 4; four times 4 = 16; a quarter of 16 = 4; and three times 4 = 12.

Alternatively, think $3 \times \frac{1}{4} \times 4 \times \frac{1}{3} \times 12$ and simplify to leave 12.

V2 B 8

Pupils will see the rule in different ways. "Sum of the top two numbers = product of the bottom two". Or "Multiply the bottom left number by the bottom right, then subtract the top left to give the top right". For ? = 8, then we can check: $7 \times 8 - 5 = 54$.

V3 E 81

The sum of the digits of the number 81 is 9, which is its square root.

V4 A 0

The number must be 1725 which is a multiple of 3 but not 2. When divided by 5 the remainder is 0.

If 172❂ is a multiple of two and not a multiple of three, we get three possibilities with three different remainders when they are divided by five. So a small change in the question gives a problem with three correct answers!

V5 D 19

The first few prime numbers are 2, 3, 5, 7, 11, 13 and 17. 19 can be written as $19 = 3 + 5 + 11$ (the sum of three different primes).

V6 C 4

The largest suggested answer is 8, so the largest number being considered is $8^3 = 512$. The cube numbers up to 512 are 1, 8, 27, 64, 125, 216, 343 and 512 itself. The only square number is 64. Now $4^3 = 8^2$, so $a = 4$.

Very challenging problems – Answers and Notes

V7 D 6

Powers of 2 are 2, 4, 8, 16, 32, 64, 128, 256 ... The final digits follow the pattern 2, 4, 8, 6 and so on. As 2^{100} will come to the end of a group of 4, it will end in 6.

Pupils could do a project on the last digits of other powers. They could write down a rule which allows them to find the last digit of any whole number raised to an integral power. Here are the repeating patterns:

powers of 2: 2, 4, 8, 6	powers of 3: 3, 9, 7, 1
powers of 4: 4, 6, 4, 6	powers of 5: 5, 5, 5, 5
powers of 6: 6, 6, 6, 6	powers of 7: 7, 9, 3, 1
powers of 8: 8, 4, 2, 6	powers of 9: 9, 1, 9, 1.

V8 D 28

Factors of 28 are 1, 2, 4, 7, 14 (and 28):
$1 + 2 + 4 + 7 + 14 = 28$.

V9 C 13

$1001 = 7 \times 11 \times 13$. So the age of the oldest child is 13 years.

What happens if the ages of the three children when multiplied together come to these numbers: 1320, 1331 ?

V10 C 38

$325 = 5 \times 5 \times 13$. So the two 2-digit numbers must have been 13 and 25. The addition $13 + 25$ gives 38.

In this question, Illtyd got an initial answer of 325. With this number we could work out the one pair of numbers he used. How about using 324, 323, 322 or 321? Some maths problems have no answers, one answer or more than one answer.

Very challenging problems – Answers and Notes

V11 C   1312

The largest two digits must go in the two tens columns. So the possibilities are 41 and 32, and 42 and 31.

A larger answer will be gained by putting the 2 with 30, getting 2 40s rather than 2 30s. So the best pair is 41 and 32 giving 1312.

What is the smallest number that can be made with the 1, 2, 3 and 4 in 2-digit numbers? Can your pupils generalise, indicating how the smallest and largest numbers can be found with two 3-digit numbers using 1 to 6, and so on?

V12 E   7, 6, 5, 5, 12

The numbers in A, B, C and D can be eliminated immediately as they do not have both a median of 6 and a mode of 5. The numbers in E do. A calculation will show the numbers in E also have a mean of 7.

V13 D   26

Of the four numbers, two must be 7 (mode). If the median is 10, the third number must be 13 (taking the mean of the central two numbers). To get a mean of 15 the numbers must add up to 60; the fourth number must be 33. So the range is $33 - 7 = 26$.

V14 B $\frac{2}{9}$

If all six faces have three equal rectangles (giving 18 rectangles in all) then four out of eighteen are black.

So the fraction shaded black is $\frac{2}{9}$.

V15 B $\frac{4}{11}$

$\frac{4}{10}$ is 0.4; and $\frac{4}{12}$ is $\frac{1}{3}$ or 0.3333.... The given decimal (0.363636...) is between 0.4 and 0.3333.... So the answer must be $\frac{4}{11}$. Pupils can check by calculating the first few decimal places when dividing 4 by 11.

V16 C   19

Cutting 5 mm off both sides will leave a square piece of bread of $9\,\text{cm} \times 9\,\text{cm}$. The original area was $100\ \text{cm}^2$ so the area removed is $19\ \text{cm}^2$. The percentage removed is therefore 19%. How big would the crust need to be to remove 50% of the area of the bread?

Very challenging problems – Answers and Notes

V17 B   25%

Suppose Bob's pocket money was £1 a week. Reducing it by 20% would give him 80p a week. To increase his pocket money from 80p to £1 means he needs a 25% increase to change the 80p back to £1.

This is the classic problem: reduce a number by 50%, then increase the answer by 50%. Has the number returned to the original value? No!

Pupils could try more examples, using a calculator.

V18 D   6:1

Ratio of Jack to Jim is 1:4.
Ratio of Jim to John is 2:3 which is 4:6.
The ratio of Jack:John is 1 : 6, and so John:Jack is 6 : 1.

V19 C   720

The recipe is for three people, but Dwight is cooking for twenty-seven people. So he needs nine times the quantities of the recipe. So he needs 9×80 g $= 720$ g of sugar.

V20 B   Q

The ratio of the speeds of the two trains is $12:20 = 3:5$.
The track has been divided into 8 parts so the trains will pass each other $\frac{3}{8}$ of the way from Y to Z; i.e. at Q.

V21 A   two triangles

Pairs of shapes B and C can be made by joining the vertex of one triangle to another vertex, pair D from joining two points on adjacent sides, pair E from joining one vertex to a point on one of the other sides.

V22 E   all the same

Every diagram involves moving around the perimeter 2 lots of 8 cm vertically and two lots of 5 cm horizontally. The perimeters therefore are of the same total length.

If the small lengths on the slope are increased in number and therefore reduced in size, the total length of this slope remains

Very challenging problems – Answers and Notes

the same. This slope will gradually look like a straight line (like a diagonal) but it isn't. The total length of all these small pieces is still more than the length of the diagonal.

V23 D   9.6

If the height of the flag is 2.4 m then the width of each rectangle must be 2.4 ÷ 3 = 0.8 m. The length of the flag is 0.8 + 0.8 + 2.4 = 4 m. The area is therefore 4 m × 2.4 m = 9.6 m^2.

V24 D   32

The area of the square is four times that of the triangle: 64 cm^2. So the length of one side of the square is 8 cm. The perimeter is therefore 32 cm. It is possible to use Pythagoras' Theorem but this method is more complicated.

V25 C   0.1 mm

Thinking mathematically, the cylinder of paint in the tin is being changed into a flat thin cuboid with base area 10 m^2. Choosing centimetres (to try to minimise the zeros!) the volume of the cylinder of paint is 1000 m^3.
The area of the wall is 10 cm × 10 000 cm = 100 000 cm^2. So the thickness of the paint is $\frac{1000}{100\,000}$ = 0.01 cm = 0.1 mm.

V26 E   49

Horizontally, on the top square, there are 8 lines. Three horizontal layers give 24 lines. Vertically (and parallel to the sides of the cube) there are five more lines on each plane giving 15 more lines. Vertically and parallel to the front of the cube are 6 more diagonal lines, and diagonally across the cube there are 4 more: total 49 lines.

V27 B   B

The volumes of these containers are:
A 500   B 512   C less than 10 × 10 × 5; i.e. less than 500
D 480   E 216 + 125 + 64 + 27 + 8 + 1 = 441.
So the conatiner which holds the most water is B.

Very challenging problems – Answers and Notes

V28 A 50

Making a smaller scale model of Big Ben will mean halving all three dimensions and using one eighth of 400 g, i.e. 50 g of plasticine.

Pupils can check this 'eighth' rule by calculating the volume of some cubes (and other shapes) and comparing them with the volumes of the half-size shapes.

V29 B 125

Each side of the small box is half of the larger box so the volume of the smaller box will be one-eighth that of the larger. So the smaller box will hold $1000 \div 8 = 125$ buttons.

V30 C 18

Pupils can approach this problem in several ways:

a) continue the pattern until they get 64 small squares, and then count the lines (18).

b) create and complete a table:
number of straight lines: 4 6 8 10 12 14 16 18
number of small squares: 1 4 9 16 25 36 49 64

c) a few pupils might get to a formula: if l is the number of lines and s is the number of squares then $l = 2(\sqrt{s} + 1)$ giving $l = 18$.

Can your pupils justify the formula by thinking through how it was created? For example, in this pattern there are $\sqrt{s}$ squares in each row and therefore $\sqrt{s} + 1$ vertical lines. Therefore there are $2(\sqrt{s} + 1)$ lines in each drawing. They could find and justify formulas in other simple patterns.

V31 B 3

The left diagram needs five extra shaded squares (and has four lines of symmetry) but the right diagram needs only three extra shaded squares to give two lines of symmetry.

66

Very challenging problems – Answers and Notes

V32 E   **2.4 m**

Pupils may use ratios to solve this. The father's shadow is $2 \times \frac{180}{150} = 2.4$ m. Some pupils might see that, using 180 and 150, the father's shadow can be calculated by multiplying by 6 and dividing by 5. Or use $\frac{150}{180} = \frac{200}{?}$.

V33 A $\frac{1}{8}$

A simple but long-winded approach is to list all (equally-likely) possibilities using T = top, L = left, R = right: (**bold** indicates a burst balloon)

TLR **T**LR T**L**R TL**R** **TL**R **T**L**R** T**LR** **TLR**

There are 8 possibilities (all equally likely), so the probability that all 3 balloons are burst is $\frac{1}{8}$.

Using probability theory, the probability that all three balloons burst is $\frac{1}{2} \times \frac{1}{2} \times \frac{1}{2} = \frac{1}{8}$.

A probability diagram could be used to solve this problem and many others. For example, what is the probability of two of the three balloons being burst?

Multiplication is used along the tree, and addition to add up the probabilities at the ends of the branches.

V34 E   **24**

Lots! Pupils could draw and colour in lots of teddies or could make a list using a code like two shirts called A and B, three trousers called P, Q and R and hats W, X, Y and Z. The list could start APW, BPW, ...

This gives $N = 2 \times 3 \times 4 = 24$.

A simpler example would be if Teddy had two suits and three hats. By listing all possibilities, pupils can see there are six different arrangements. With the 2 shirts, 3 pairs of trousers and 4 hats, a very organised list must be made if possibilities are not left out. With several examples using thoughtful lists, pupils will see the general rule for calculating the number of possibilities.

Very challenging problems – Answers and Notes

V35 C 12

The possibilities are:

$$1966, 1696, 1669, 9166, 9616, 9661,$$
$$6619, 6169, 6196, 6691, 6961, 6916.$$

If the four digits on the security code were different, there would be $4 \times 3 \times 2 \times 1$ arrangements. But as two digits are the same, that number is reduced by half to 12. Pupils could list the numbers for codes with a larger number of digits, maybe some with repeating digits, and check using the rules given above.

V36 D 6

Pupils can work out how many ways there are to each point by imagining the paths the balls can take as they fall. In fact, the number of ways balls can get to any point is shown in this pattern.

```
          1
        1   1
      1   2   1
    1   3   3   1
  1   4   6   4   1
```

The pattern of numbers shown above is Pascal's triangle. Pupils will meet this pattern later in mathematics lessons when working on combinations and on the binomial theorem. Notice that the numbers in each row add up to a power of 2.

V37 A $\frac{1}{8}$

$\frac{2}{5} + \frac{1}{10} = \frac{1}{2}$. So the sum of the probabilities for the other four outcomes is also $\frac{1}{2}$; that means each probability is $\frac{1}{8}$.

V38 C $\frac{3}{5}$

	First bag	Second bag
At the start:	12 blue	12 red
Then:	6 blue	12 red + 6 blue
Then:	6 blue + 6 red + 3 blue	6 red + 3 blue
	= 9 blue + 6 red	

So in the first bag there are $\frac{9}{15}$ blue balls, i.e. $\frac{3}{5}$.

Pupils could work through this problem with more balls in the bags; for example, try 24 balls in each bag, and then 100. In fact, even if liquid is used, the fraction remains $\frac{3}{5}$. Pupils could also try to create other similar problems.

Very challenging problems – Answers and Notes

V39 B **1 000 000 minutes**

Two years old gives
2 × 52 weeks = 104 weeks =104 × 7 days = 728 days
= 728 × 24 hours = 17 472 hours = 17 472 × 60 minutes
= 1 048 320 minutes = 1 048 320 × 60 seconds
= 62899200 seconds.

V40 E **Z**

Pupils will probably use intuition here, but they
will see that they are adding 4 mph across the
river with 4 mph down the river. So Ian will
end up at point Z.

Once pupils have understood the (vector) triangle
in this problem, they can find out what happens in
similar but more complicated cases using accurate
drawing. For example, in which direction would
Ian swim if he swum at 4 mph and the river
flowed at 3 mph? (This is the start of vectors,
mathematics in which quantities have direction!)

V41 A **21**

Pupils could test the suggested answers. Or use an equation. If x
is my age, then $x + 4 = 5(x - 16)$. So $4x = 84$ giving $x = 21$.

V42 C **7**

$K \times H = H$ tells us that $K = 1$.
$F \times H = T1$ tells us that $H = 3$ or 7 as $T1$ must be 21.
With $H \times H = RC$, H cannot be 3 and so must be 7.
Replacing letters with numbers gives $3 \times 7 = 21$, $1 \times 7 = 7$
and $7 \times 7 = 49$.

V43 E **40**

Working through the suggested answers gives 40.
Working backwards from the final (swallowed) sweet gives

$$1 \to 3 \to 4 \to 12 \to 13 \to 39 \to 40 \,!$$

Pupils could work through the problem using half instead of two-
thirds each time, or again three-quarters. (Answers: 15 and 85.)

Very challenging problems – Answers and Notes

V44 D 61

We are looking for a number which is one more that a multiple of 2, 3, 4 and 5. The smallest such multiple is 60, so there are 61 pupils in the school.

Here are a few similar questions. How many pupils in another (larger) school if one pupil is left out when pupils are lined up in 2s, 3s, 4s, 5s, and 6s? Now add 7s. Add 8s. Can pupils tell you a general rule for saying how many pupils in a school when one pupil has been left out of different lines?

V45 C 5

The first few perfect cubes are 1, 8, 27, 64, 125 and 216. The cat ate two leaving a square number. $27 - 2 = 25$.

Subtracting 2 from the other cubes does not give a square number. So there must have been 5 little cubes in each side of the square.

V46 E 36

Pupils will probably list the totals which cannot be made with these coins. A few pupils may spot the pattern and take a short cut! The missing totals are: 4, 9, 14, 19, 24, 29, 34, 39, 40 - 49, 54, 59, 64, 69, 74, 79, 84, 89, 90 - 99.

What is the smallest number of coins that could be added to this set so that all quantities from 1p to 99p could be made?

Can your pupils develop a set of coins which can make all numbers from 1 to 99?   Maybe they thought of 1p, 2p, 4p, 8p, 16p, 32p and 64p – the powers of 2 again!

V47 D 110

The next palindrome is 2112 which is 110 years after 2002.

Very challenging problems – Answers and Notes

V48 C   11

	5	9	11	12	16
It was even				#	#
It was odd	#	#	#		
It was prime	#		#		
It was a square number					#
It has two digits			#	#	#
It was between 6 and 14		#	#	#	

Four correct statements means 11 must be the winning number.

V49 B   2

150 gm of butter is needed. We use the approx. 1 oz – 25 gm.
So we need about 6 ounces; that is two packets of butter.

V50 E   toast

Pupils can calculate the price of the items:
sausage = 40p, chips = 80p, egg = 100p so toast = 0p.
Café owners may not use maths to fix prices but your pupils
could make up some menus and prices of their own. They could
also check up on local prices!

V51 D   70 p

There are various ways of tackling this problem. Adding the
equations gives 5 samousas and 5 pakoras costing £6. Therefore
one of each costs £1.20 and two of each costs £2.40. Comparing
this with the original two sentences gives a pakora at 70p and a
samousa at 50p.

The problem has a symmetry, with 3, 2 and 2, 3. The method
below can be used to solve simultaneous equations, with or
without that symmetry:

$$2s + 3p = 310 \ (\times 3) \Rightarrow 6s + 9p = 930$$
$$3s + 2p = 290 \ (\times 2) \Rightarrow 6s + 4p = 580$$
$$\text{so} \quad 5p = 350 \Rightarrow p = 70, s = 60.$$

Very challenging problems – Answers and Notes

V52 B 8

Not easy! Pupils might start using 'trial and error'. Or they could start with 357p, and keep taking away 13 until they get a multiple of 30. Alternatively, pupils might realize that multiples of 30 end in 0, so the money spent on 13p balloons must end in 7. This leads to 117p on 13p balloons. An equation will do it. If l is the number of large balloons, then
$30l + (17 - l) \times 13 = 357$. So $17l = 136$ and $l = 8$.
Any other methods?

In fact, the number of balloons bought in this problem (17) is superfluous. But in a similar problem with different numbers, the number of balloons bought might be needed. If balloons cost 5p and 6p, and the total costs was 70p, either a total of 12 or 13 balloons could be bought. Can pupils find a problem with three different answers?

V53 C 21

If all these creatures had seven legs there will be about $150 \div 7$ creatures; i.e. about 21. There are three more 'nits than 'gnats, so possible pairs might include 7 'gnats 10 'nits, 8 'gnats 11 'nits, 9 'gnats 12 'nits, 10 'gnats 13 'nits. Calculations show that the third pair gives 150 legs.
Suppose there are n nanognats. There will be $n + 23$ nanonits.
So $6n + 8(n + 3) = 150, 14n = 126$, so $n = 9$.
So there are 21 insects.

V54 A 7

There are 40 ears and so there are 20 bodies. If there were 10 of each there would be 60 legs. We need 6 more. So try 3 more dogs. Seven people and thirteen dogs gives $14 + 52 = 66$ legs. Using algebra, if there were n people then
$2n + 4(20 - n) = 66$ giving $n = 7$.

Pupils could try these. How many people were there in the park if there were 40 ears and 60 legs; or 40 ears and 80 legs; or 40 ears and 40 legs; or 40 ears and 160 legs; or 40 ears and 65 legs?

Very challenging problems – Answers and Notes

V55 B   72 cm²

Eighteen 2 cm × 2 cm squares make up the surface area of this solid. The surface area is therefore $18 \times 4 = 72\,(\text{cm}^2)$. Can pupils find and object with a larger number of cubes with the same surface area? (Yes, for example a 3 × 2 array.) Investigate.

V56 B   10

A strange problem. If R and A denote the number of flies caught by SylvesteR and SylviA, then we have the equation:

$\frac{1}{2}R + 10 = A + \frac{1}{2}R$.

This gives $A = 10$. So Sylvia caught 10 flies. We don't know how many flies Sylvester caught.

This is a strange problem in that we can find out how many flies Sylvia caught but can never know how many flies Sylvester caught. Can your pupils think of any other problems like this? Send such problems in to the PMC problems Team if they can!

V57 D   24

Pupils can try different combinations to get the different answers. $7 + 11 = 18$; $9 + 11 = 20$; $5 + 7 + 11 = 23$ and $7 + 9 + 11 = 27$. It is not possible to score 24 with these bunnies. The numbers on the bunnies are all odd numbers, so either two or four numbers are needed to get 24. The largest total hitting two bunnies is $9 + 11 = 20$ (too small) and using all four bunnies gives $5 + 7 + 9 + 11 = 32$ (too big) so 24 is impossible.

Can your pupils work out all the total scores (up to 32) which are impossible to get? It might be easier to list methodically all the total scores that can be obtained.

(Impossible scores are 1, 2, 3, 4, 6, 8, 10, 13, 15, 17, 19, 22, 24, 26, 28, 29, 30 and 31.)

V58 B   Q

The rifle hits bunny P, then (4 sec later) T, then S then R and finally Q.

Which bunny would be left if the air rifle shoots every second, or every two seconds, or three seconds, or five seconds? What would happen if there were 10 bunnies (taking 10 seconds to go round once) and the rifle fires every four seconds?

Very challenging problems – Answers and Notes

V59 C   hare

If the competitors all started exactly opposite the marks on the track (which relate to their speeds), then they would all finish together. But the cheetah starts behind its mark and the hare in front. So the hare will win.

An assumption that they can get to maximum speed instantaneously has been made!

V60 A   1 minute

The first two sentences show that it takes half a second to rewind 10 seconds of tape. So, to rewind 20 minutes will take $6 \times 20 \times \frac{1}{2} = 60$ and 60 seconds is 1 minute.

V61 A   Delores 3 coins and Lavinia 6 coins.

The nine bottles were shared among the three people evenly, so Delores gave Paulette 1 bottle and Lavinia gave Paulette 2 bottles (ratio 1 : 2). The fairest way of dividing the payment of nine coins is to give Delores 3 coins and Lavinia 6 coins (ratio 1 : 2).

V62 C   10 minutes

If t is the time in minutes before Henrietta runs out then

$$100 + 10t - 20t = 0 \Rightarrow 10t = 100 \Rightarrow t = 10$$

so she takes 10 minutes.

Mathematical purists (and chocoholics) will correctly say that Henrietta runs out 3 seconds before 10 minutes. She has then finished her last chocolate (3 seconds for each) but the machine hasn't yet produced the next chocolate (taking 6 seconds each). Pupils could draw a graph which shows how many chocolates there are against time.

Time (mins)	0	1	2	3	4	5...
Beginning:	100	100	100	100	100	100
Eaten:	0	20	40	60	80	100
Made by machine:	0	10	20	30	40	50
Chocolates available:	100	90	80	70	60	50

Pupils could develop a set of rules or formula which will calculate the time before Henrietta runs out if the constants in the

Very challenging problems – Answers and Notes

problem are varied. If s is the initial number of chocolates, m is the rate produced by the machine and e the rate at which Henrietta eats, the time until she runs out is (approximately) given by $t = \dfrac{s}{(e - m)}$.

V63 B **11**

One way is to make a table.

number of days	4	8	12	16
number of tins	3	6	9	12

So 11 tins are needed.

Ratios could be used. Tins needed $= 14 \times \frac{3}{4} = 10\frac{1}{2}$ tins ? 11 tins.

Pupils could draw a graph for this information. Not all graphs have straight lines or curves (e.g. a graph showing the cost of posting parcels of different weights).

Here are some others: the number of 5-seater taxis for different numbers of people; the number of 6-bottle boxes needed to pack bottles of squash.

V64 D **15th day**

In one day Gnasher eats half a can and Nibbles eats one fifth. This makes $\frac{7}{10}$ of a can each day. After 10 days, 7 tins will have been finished. On the 14th day, I will have served $14 \times \frac{7}{10} = 9\frac{8}{10}$ cans. But I only had 10 cans, so on the fifteenth day I will need more. Using algebra, if x is the number of days the cans will last, $0.7 \times x = 10$ giving $x = 14.3$. So I will need more food on the fifteenth day.

V65 D **500**

She set up 303 628 dominoes in 13×45 hours. So the calculation needed is $303\,628 \div (13 \times 45)$. $300\,000 \div 600$ gives approximately 500.

This problem contains more information than is needed to answer the question. Which are the extra bits of information? What other problems could have been asked with all this information?

Very challenging problems – Answers and Notes

V66 B 5

15 fights @ $2\frac{1}{2}$ silver pieces = $37\frac{1}{2}$ pieces. $12\frac{1}{2}$ more are needed. That is 5 more fights.

V67 D 6

One day, Addum is infected. On day 1, three more people are infected. So we get:

Day 0: just Addum infected   Day 1: $3 (+1) = 4$
Day 2: $9 (+ 4) = 13$ Day 3: $27 (+13) = 40$
Day 4: $81 (+ 40) = 121$ Day 5: $243 (+121) = 364$
Day 6: $729 (+ 364) = 1093$ people infected.

If each infected person infects three more other people every day, how long will it take to infect a million people? Or everyone in the world, about 6000 million (21 days). A basic calculator with a long display can work this out. For humans this sounds alarming! What practical matters would reduce this rate of infection? (Medical prevention, problems of the virus finding three new people in a highly infected environment, the virus crossing oceans etc.)

Thanks

This book was compiled by Peter Bailey. Many teachers have worked on PMC problems over the years. Thanks go to Colin Abell, Anthony Carter, Meryl Hargreaves, Lesley Jones, Rudolf Loewenstein, Howard Maxstead, Robyn Pickles, John Place, Ruth Swinton and Margaret Williams. Thank you to Rudolf, again, and to Richard Kirby, for looking through drafts and for your comments and ideas. Thanks also to Bill Richardson for his work on the PMC and in formatting this book.

The Primary Mathematics Challenge is currently sponsored by Invicta Education.

The Primary Mathematics Challenge

The problems in this book are taken from the Primary Mathematics Challenge (PMC) papers from November 2002 to February 2006.

The PMC is aimed at school pupils aged 11 or less. In September and October, schools order packs of ten challenge papers (which include Answers and Notes and certificates for everyone). Pupils take the challenge at any time during the month of November. The top scoring pupils are then invited to take the PMC Finals in the following February. Questions from these finals are included in this book. For further information, visit the PMC pages on the MA website (www.m-a.org.uk). The problems set in the PMC Finals are very difficult for primary-aged pupils, and therefore will also challenge younger secondary pupils.

PMC Live On-Line

Two PMC papers can be taken live on line on the MA website.

Primary Maths Problems On-Line

There are also some more PMC problems live on the MA website.
These can be accessed directly by pupils from school or home. Pupils select one of four levels, and are given five problems at that level from the problems bank. Their responses are 'marked' and a certificate provided.

Secondary Maths Problems On-Line

There are more similar problems for secondary school pupils (aged 11 years and above) on the MA website, formatted in the same way as the Primary Maths Problems On-Line.

The Mathematical Association,

MATHEMATICAL ASSOCIATION

supporting mathematics in education

formed in 1871, works to support and improve the teaching of mathematics. It is represented on all major bodies concerned with mathematics education in the UK and has wide influence through its members, publications and activities.bodies concerned with mathematics education in the UK and has wide influence through its members, publications and activities.

WHO ARE OUR MEMBERS?

Teachers in primary and secondary schools, lecturers in further and higher education, advisers, inspectors, practising mathematicians, students, libraries and other institutions. We currently have some 5000 members, not just in the UK but throughout the world.

WHAT DO YOU GET FOR YOUR MONEY?

An option of 6 categories of membership depending on the journals you select. In addition, we publish a comprehensive range of books and reports. We organise a range of meetings and conferences throughout the UK and provide other services for members such as an annual conference, local branches, access to the Association's library, a newsletter, occasional free reports and teaching materials, a problem bureau, a one third discount on the price of publications, professional development opportunities, the chance to work in small groups investigating specific aspects of mathematics, and a primary mathematics challenge.

HOW TO JOIN

Reach us in the following ways:
The Mathematical Association
259 London Road   Leicester
LE2 3BE   United Kingdom
Tel: ++ 44 [0]116 221 0013 Fax: ++ 44 [0]116 212 2835
Email: office@m-a.org.uk Website: www.m-a.org.uk